Jane Cousins was born in Lond
University of Kent. She worke
Churchill's biographer, from 1
Harold Wilson from 1971-73
Television's 'World in Action
Granada's daily local news pro
the Sexual Law Reform Societ, ... _
and the Arts Society, and has lectured on censorship and the
media, sexual law reform, and trades unionism. A freelance
journalist, her first book, *Turkey: Torture and Persecution*, was
published in 1973. Her interest in sex education led her to
working with teenagers, their parents and teachers on the subject
and to presenting a weekly sex phone-in programme for
Manchester's Piccadilly Radio. At present she is organiser of the
Edinburgh International Television Festival, British representative
of a Finnish publishing house, and is working on her next book.
She lives in Hale, Cheshire.

VIRAGO
is a feminist publishing company:

"It is only when women start to organize
in large numbers that we become a
political force, and begin to move towards
the possibility of a truly democratic society
in which every human being can be brave,
responsible, thinking and diligent in the struggle
to live at once freely and unselfishly"

SHEILA ROWBOTHAM
Women, Resistance and Revolution

VIRAGO
Advisory Group

Make it happy

What Sex is All About

Jane Cousins

Line Drawings by
Susan Hunter

Virago

London

Published by Virago Limited 1978
5 Wardour Street, London W1V 3HE

Copyright © Jane Cousins 1978

ISBN 0 86068 037 1

Printed in Great Britain by Unwin Brothers
Limited, The Gresham Press, Old Woking,
Surrey

CONTENTS

Acknowledgements

1 Our sex lives   1
In childhood, reaching maturity, puberty, adolescence

2 Our bodies   5
What we look like, outer sex organs, inner sex organs — girls, periods, sanitary towels and tampons, what it feels like to have a period, inner sex organs — boys, ejaculating, wet dreams, egg and sperm together, getting pregnant

3 Who am I?   22
Sexual identity, homosexuality, bisexuality, feminine and masculine stereotyping

4 Masturbation   27
The myths, how girls masturbate, how boys masturbate, can masturbating do any harm or good?

5 Orgasms   32
Getting turned on, having an orgasm, not having an orgasm

6 Enjoying sex   37
Petting, drawing the line, sex without pregnancy, foreplay, intercourse, positions

7 It isn't always easy   45
Virginity, the first time, sex aids

8 Birth control 51
Conception, contraception, the myths, whose responsibility? where to get contraceptives, reliable methods; the Pill, IUD, sheath, diaphragm plus spermicides; unreliable methods; rhythm, withdrawal, holding back, douche; sterilisation, the future

9 Pregnancy 69
How to tell, pregnancy testing, who to tell

10 Abortion 75
How safe? how to get one, methods of abortion, afterwards

11 Having a baby 81
Where to stay, leaving home, medical care, finding out about pregnancy and childbirth, living together, marriage, adoption and fostering, education, work, money, rights of the father, maintenance

12 Looking after our bodies 87
Hygiene, sexually transmitted diseases, where to get treatment, contact tracing, gonorrhoea, syphilis, vaginal infections, urethritis, crabs, scabies, herpes, cystitis, circumcision, tight foreskin, discharges, testicles, periods, cancer

13 Sex and the law 102
Legal attitudes to sex, age of consent, anal intercourse, bestiality, exhibitionism, homosexuality, incest, paedophilia, pornography & censorship, prostitution, rape, transexuality, tranvestism, voyeurism, dealing with the law, what to do in court, where to go for legal advice

Useful addresses

Booklist

Index

It's impossible for me to thank everyone enough for all their help and support. But special thanks to Bobbie Crosby for the picture research; Thelma McGough for researching the useful addresses and further information; and, for their photographs, Nina Kellgren (photos on page 12), Pete Mackertitch (photos on pages 9, 16, 58) and Roy Cuthbert (photo on page 99).

I should also like to give warm thanks to: Rose Ades, Pam Adshead, Margaret Branch, the Brook Advisory Centre, Shirley Clarke, Cathy Crawford, the Campaign for Homosexual Equality. Tess Gill, Judy Gray, Bob Greaves, Jim Greaves, Antony Grey, Gail Hamilton, Pat Hawes, Sylvia Jones, Charles Kitchen, Jonathan Lawton, Jill Liddington, Trevor Locke, Joyce Mastin, Diane Mundy, the National Association of One Parent Families, Pam Peart, Michael Rubinstein, Eleanor Stephens, The Women's National Cancer Control Campaign, Lynne Wright. And my thanks also to Virago, who haven't been simply my publishers but also my friends — and especially to Ursula Owen.

The publishers and author would like to thank the following for supplying illustrations, and giving permission to reproduce them: Ronald Grant for the illustrations on pages 6 and 7, Mike Jarvis for illustrations on pages 21 and 24, the Health Education Council for illustrations on pages 52, 53 and 91, 20th Century-Fox films for illustrations on pages 6 and 7.

The book is for Jim, Chris and Katie.

Our sex lives

Some people think that we shouldn't be taught anything about sex until we're adults – perhaps because they think young people shouldn't have a sex life. But sex isn't something that suddenly happens when we reach a certain age, and it isn't just for adults. Though it's obviously a bit difficult to prove, our sex lives probably start even before we're born. It's known for certain that many boys are born with an erect penis, and although it's not so easy to tell when girls first show signs of being sexually active, there's no reason to believe it's any later than for boys.

From birth onwards a lot is known about our sex lives. Both girls and boys can reach a peak of sexual excitement before they're six months old, and most of us, though by no means all, touch our sex organs for pleasure throughout our childhood. Many of the games that small children play are very sexual. Games like 'doctors' and 'mothers and fathers' often end up with kids getting good sexual feelings by touching themselves and each other. Literally millions of kids have played these games without ever coming to the slightest harm. But many parents are still convinced that these games are wrong, dangerous, or both, and try to stop children from playing with their sex organs.

Sex is a natural part of our lives whatever our age. A slap on the hand to stop us from touching our sex organs when we're young can cause a lot of harm because it makes us feel guilty and scared about our sex organs and our sexual feelings. It can make us grow up thinking that sex is wrong and in some way dirty. In fact, touching ourselves, finding out how our bodies look and work sexually, and getting sexual feelings can't do us any harm at all. And growing up feeling guilty, ashamed or scared of sex doesn't do us any good at all.

One of the most important things to learn about sex is that it's a healthy and natural part of our lives. But that doesn't mean that everyone *has* to have an active sex life. Some people find that sex is a very big part of their lives. Others prefer life with very little sex or none at all. We may find out at an early age that we want to enjoy sex, or we may find it all very unimportant until we're much older. People have sex for a variety of reasons. It can be

1

because they're curious, because it seems like a good way of expressing friendship and affection, because they want some fun or because they're in love. But you can also be curious, friendly, have fun or be in love and *not* have sex. Each one of us has different sexual feelings and needs and these can change and vary throughout our lives. There may be lots of reasons why people don't want a sexual relationship. It could be because they're not in love, because they don't want it with a certain person or simply because they don't feel like it.

It never makes sense to lie to anyone about your sexual feelings though it's often quite difficult not to. Sometimes people feel under pressure to have sex when they don't really want to. And telling someone you love them when you don't, simply in order to persuade them to have sex with you, isn't just dishonest, it can be harmful. It could give them a hang-up about sex for the rest of their lives.

It may seem to you that everyone is having a gloriously happy sex life and that you're the only person in the world who doesn't seem to have any sexual feelings – or any sex life. People of all ages can feel left out in this way. The truth most likely is that your friends are all trying to give the impression that they're sexually active and experienced when in fact they're just as unsure of themselves as you are .

What we do all need is the basic factual information about sex so that we can make our own decision about whether we want sex and, if we do, how and who with. You only have to read the advice columns in the papers and in magazines to realize how many thousands of people there are who are desperately unhappy because they've been kept in ignorance about sex. They're not known as 'agony' columns for nothing. Most of this unhappiness is caused not because people have sex but because they don't know enough about the subject. No advice column, no book, can automatically solve everyone's sex problems but there are a lot of people who could solve their own problems if only they had a little more information. Sex can and does make a lot of people very happy.

This book will give you some of the necessary basic information about sex, how some of the problems can be avoided and where to go if you need more help and advice. It's written for teenagers, their parents and teachers and for anyone else who wants to know the basic facts. Girls and boys who want to find out what sex may be all about when they're older, and older girls and boys who perhaps aren't sure what it could be all about, should be able to learn from *Make It Happy* how they can safely ignore many of the myths about sex which often make it unnecessarily complicated.

You won't find a great deal about love, or about what it feels like to be in love. This isn't because emotions aren't important – they are, very. Love is a complicated subject. And in the end no one can easily tell you what your feelings for someone are. Only you can work that out.

Sex may be a natural instinct – but learning how to express your sexual feelings doesn't always come so very naturally. It is important to remember that when it comes to sex we are all different and separate individuals. And sex isn't just about getting pleasure – it's also about giving pleasure. Mostly, however, it's about sharing pleasure. This means treating your partner honestly, fairly, and lovingly. That's the only way to make it happy.

Reaching maturity

We're all born with sex organs. A baby girl has a vagina, a uterus called a womb, and two ovaries. A baby boy has a penis, two testicles called balls, and all his internal sex organs. Throughout childhood these stay more or less as they were at birth.

But as we approach maturity our bodies start to produce natural chemicals called hormones, which alter the shape and appearance of our bodies and which make our internal sex organs become sexually mature. Reaching puberty means reaching the point when our sex organs have matured, and when girls and boys are capable of having babies.

It's impossible for anyone to know when these changes will start to happen – no two people ever mature at exactly the same age. On average girls are sexually mature about a year before boys. The average age for girls is about 11-13 and for boys it's about 12-14. But this is only the average and it can start to happen as early as 9 or 10 or as late as 17 or 18. No one really knows why some of us are early developers and others are late developers. It's known that girls and boys who have a healthy balanced diet tend to develop earlier. But it's mostly to do with the sort of body we've inherited from our parents – and there's nothing anyone can do to alter that.

We can't control the length of time it takes for our bodies to mature either. At first the hormones are produced only very irregularly. It takes time for them to be produced on a steady, balanced and regular basis. Some of us become physically and sexually mature very quickly, others find it takes several years.

After puberty comes adolescence. Technically, adolescence means growing up emotionally and mentally. But the phrase 'grown up' can mean different things to different people. We're often made to think that we have to be 'grown up' long before we really feel like it and many people feel that they're growing up all their lives. But it is true that, as in puberty our hormones take time to settle down, so in adolescence our thoughts and feelings take time to sort themselves out as well.

Some adolescent girls and boys find themselves falling in and out of love – or think that they're falling in and out of love – all the time. We often get sudden crushes or strong feelings of sexual attraction and desire for someone of the same or opposite sex. It might be a crush on an older girl or boy at school, a teacher, a pop star, a footballer or a friend. Often these feelings fade away after a few weeks or months but at the time it's not so easy to tell the difference between a sudden short crush and a deeper, stronger, perhaps more lasting feeling of love. Some girls and boys find it easier than others to cope with what can be very intense and even bewildering feelings. Certainly, the first time it happens most find it all rather frightening. You can usually

3

understand it all much more easily by the time you've fallen for your third, fourth or fifth pop star. But when you know, or think you know, that you're in love, it doesn't exactly help to be told 'You'll grow out of it'. It doesn't feel like that at the time. And just as you might 'grow out of it', there's always the chance that you won't.

Any confusion that we might feel at this time in our lives isn't helped much by the attitude of society towards sex. On the one hand adults seem to expect young people to behave as if they have no sexual feelings at all. On the other hand these same adults encourage young people to spend their money on clothes, make-up, magazines etc, all calculated to make them less childlike and more obviously sexually attractive. Teachers and parents spend a lot of time teaching kids to grow up – children are taught to walk, talk, write, read and generally copy adult behaviour – but sex is the one thing that few children learn anything about. It's not surprising that when we do eventually become more aware of our sexuality, relationships can seem rather complicated and difficult.

When life and relationships do seem to be depressingly confused it may be useful to remember that almost everyone, whatever their age, makes the same sort of mistakes. And to realise that to some extent we are confused further by the world we live in, which encourages us to act, dress and think as if sex was part of our lives and yet often discourages us from acting on our sexual feelings.

Our bodies

The hormones that are produced in our bodies as we become mature cause some very obvious changes in the shape and appearance of our bodies. For a start we begin to grow in height and put on weight, usually quite quickly. A girl's body grows more rounded and her breasts begin to develop. Hair grows around her sex organs, under her arms and quite often on her legs and on other parts of her body. Her outer sex organs go a darker colour, become more fleshy and more sensitive to touch. Her voice goes a little deeper. A boy's penis and balls grow bigger as he reaches maturity. Hair grows around his sex organs, under his arms and eventually, although usually not until he's sixteen or so, on his face and perhaps on his chest. After a bit of wavering and squeaking, his voice breaks and goes much deeper.

Very often, while the production of these hormones is getting properly balanced the skin can get very greasy and we get a spotty complexion. Some people get spots on their backs as well. It helps to eat fresh vegetables and fruit, lean meat and fish, and to keep off puddings, butter, milk, eggs and sweets. You can buy creams and medicated soap from the chemist which help clear up the spots or, if they're really bad, your doctor should be able to prescribe some extra-strong cream. Spots, pimples and blackheads will disappear in time – squeezing and picking them only makes them worse and may leave you with a pitted skin. It isn't easy, but try to leave them alone.

You may find that you suddenly start to sweat very heavily. Clean sweat doesn't smell bad, but if it's left on your body it can soon start to smell unpleasant. Washing well once or twice a day with a medicated soap helps to prevent the smell probably better than roll-on, spray or aerosol deodorants. Many of these try to mask the smell instead of killing the bacteria on the skin which produce the smell.

All these changes can be quite frightening – especially if they happen quite fast. Older people and younger sisters and brothers often find it annoyingly funny to see the changes take place and this can make many young people feel very embarrassed indeed about the fact that, for example, their breasts are developing or that their voice seems uncontrollable. All you can do is grit your teeth and bear it – there's nothing you can do to stop the changes from taking place.

One year the fashion is for big breasts . . . (Jayne Mansfield and Rock Hunter in Oh! For a Man*)*

. . . Another year small breasts are in. (Twiggy and Christopher Gable in The Boy Friend*)*

What we look like — Girls

Breasts: Slang words for women's breasts include tits, titties, knockers, boobs, buds and pips. Most of the breast is made of fat. The rest consists of glands that produce milk after a baby is born, and tubes that carry the milk to the nipple, which is what a baby sucks when it's being breastfed. During puberty, as the breasts and nipples get bigger, the dark area around the nipple, called the aureola, also gets larger and goes a darker colour.

Most women's breasts differ slightly in shape and size from each other. The difference is often much more obvious while a girl is still growing. If she's really worried about looking lop-sided, a slightly padded bra will help to even out the difference, but the chances are that no one else will notice. It shouldn't really matter in any case — we shouldn't have to feel pressured into living up to people's idea of what is or isn't 'perfect'.

Hairs sometimes grow around the nipples or in between the breasts. Shaving off these hairs only produces an uncomfortable stubble. Although it's really nothing to worry about, if it becomes very thick and dark and you don't like it, your doctor will tell you the best way to disguise or remove it.

Most girls think that their breasts are too big, too small, too high or too droopy. The fashion pages in papers and magazines take a delight in telling us that breasts are supposed to look small one season and large the next. It's certainly one way of making us buy more clothes! The bra manufacturers obviously try to sell as many bras as possible — there are padded and wired bras for one fashion trend and wispy 'no-bra' bras for another. They can't have been too pleased when many women decided to stop wearing them altogether! If a girl feels better without a bra, then there's no point in her wearing one. If she finds that her breasts flop uncomfortably when she runs or plays games, she may prefer to wear one. It's true that if large breasts are unsupported they will eventually droop — but who's to say that drooping breasts are any worse than those that don't?

Magazines, Miss World competitions and advertisements are all geared to make us think that every girl should have perfectly shaped large breasts. (How often do you see a model with small breasts on those advertisements for cigars, rum or pots of paint?) Perhaps one day manufacturers will decide that their products are good enough to sell on their own merit, and don't need a deep cleavage in order to make people spend their money. But meanwhile this emphasis on the so-called 'perfect' large-breasted female can make many girls with small breasts feel inferior and somehow not very 'female'. And it can make girls with large breasts feel worried that their bodies are little more than toys for men to gawp at and play with.

Whether breasts are large or small makes no difference to whether you'll be able to breastfeed your baby if you want to. Nor does it make any difference to the amount of pleasure and enjoyment you'll get from them. The breasts, especially the nipples, of most girls (and some boys) are an important part of enjoying sex. The size and shape make no difference to the amount of sexual pleasure you get when they're touched, stroked or kissed.

Vulva — the outer sex organs

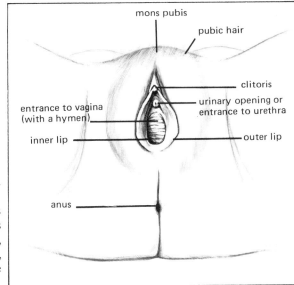

mons pubis

pubic hair

clitoris

urinary opening or entrance to urethra

entrance to vagina (with a hymen)

inner lip

outer lip

anus

Vulva: The outer sex organs of a girl are called the vulva. This consists of the mons pubis, outer lips, inner lips, clitoris, urethra and entrance to the vagina.

There are many words used instead of the technical term — fanny, cunt, pussy, quim are just some. In fact many girls don't use any word at all. And many more are brought up to think that they shouldn't touch or look at their sex organs. It's as if some people would have us believe that a girl's sex organs are dirty, unpleasant or simply don't exist. It doesn't sound strange to hear a boy talk about his penis as if it's a best friend called 'Willy' or 'John Thomas'. People tend to describe someone they don't think much of as a 'prick'. But when they *really* don't like someone they call her or him a 'cunt' — as if they think somehow a vagina is nastier than a penis. Perhaps one day girls will call their vulva by a friendly name too — although, admittedly, a 'Wilhelmina' or a 'Jane Thomasina' sounds a bit weird!

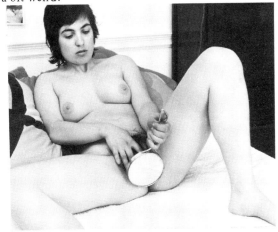

The best way for a girl to find out what her sex organs are like is to use a mirror and take a good long look

9

Mons Pubis: Another technical term for the mons pubis is the Mons Veneris. This means 'Mount of Venus' — Venus being the ancient goddess of love. The mons pubis is the slightly raised mound on which the pubic hair grows. A couple of slang words for the mons pubis are beaver and bush.

Pubic Hair: Also called pubes. It grows on the mons pubis and on the outer lips. This hair is often a much darker colour than the hair on the head.

Outer lips: The technical term is labia majora. Most of the time these lips lie close together to protect the more delicate skin and organs underneath.

Inner lips: The technical term is labia minora. When the outer lips are pushed apart the darker, thinner and slightly more slippery inner lips can be seen.

Clitoris: It consists of a head or glans (which means acorn) and a short stem or shaft. The glans is full of nerve endings which are what make the clitoris the most sensitive part of a girl's sex organs. It can usually be seen just poking out of a hood of skin at the top of the vulva where the inner lips meet. This hood or skin may have to be gently pushed back in order to see the clitoris properly. A girl who isn't sure where her clitoris is — and it's not always easy to find — should gently feel her vulva, and when she hits upon the most sensitive spot, it's pretty sure to be the clitoris. It can feel like a small sensitive bump about the size of a tiny pea.

The clitoris is made of spongy tissue with many small veins or blood vessels running through it. When a girl gets sexually excited a small ring of muscle at the base of the shaft tightens and stops the blood from flowing out. This makes the clitoris become firm and stiff and poke right out of its hood or skin. As sexual excitement dies down, the muscles relax, the blood flows in and out at the normal pace and the clitoris loses its stiffness and goes back in its hood. If all this sounds like what happens when a boy gets an erect penis — you're right. The clitoris and the penis both work in a very similar way. This is because during the very first stages of development in the womb, the tiny embryo (pronounced em-bree-o) of a girl is almost identical to that of a boy. And it's only as the embryo grows and starts developing that the cells growing into the sexual organs become the clitoris and vaginal lips in a girl, the penis and testicles in a boy.

Urethra (pronounced u-ree-thrah): This is the small opening just under the clitoris. It's also known as the pee-hole because it's connected by a tube to the bladder, inside the body, which is where pee, or urine, collects. Pee comes out of the urethra.

Entrance to the vagina: The entrance or opening to the vagina is a ring of muscle which is usually small and tight. Slang words for the vagina include slit, crack, hole, twat and bearded clam. The muscles can relax, making the entrance wide enough to let a couple of fingers up into the vagina, a penis up into the vagina during sexual intercourse, and to allow a baby to be born through it.

Hymen: Slang words include maidenhead and cherry. The entrance to the vagina may be partly or almost totally blocked by a thin layer of skin called the hymen. Some girls are born without a hymen or it may get broken at a young age quite naturally by riding a bike or horse or even by being constipated. A girl with a hymen may be able to see it in her mirror. If she can't push her fingers more than a few centimetres up into her vagina it means her hymen is still there. Some hymens have holes in them, but in any case it never completely seals off the vagina – the blood of a period will always be able to seep through.

What we look like – Boys

Penis: There are many slang words for the penis: cock, tool, prick, dick, knob, willy, John Thomas, a man's best friend, the one-eyed trouser snake are some. Like the clitoris it's made up of two parts: the head is called the glans and the long part the shaft. The glans is the most sensitive part as it has thousands of nerve endings in it.

At the very tip of the head is the opening to a tube called the urethra which runs inside through the middle of the penis. Right inside the body this tube branches into two smaller tubes, with one going to the bladder and the other to the internal sex organs. The penis is made of spongy tissue with many small veins or blood vessels in it. When it's limp and little, blood flows in and out of the penis at a steady rate. When a boy gets sexually excited the ring of muscle inside the base of the shaft tightens and blood flows into the veins but not out. This makes his penis grow big and erect. As sexual excitement dies down, the muscles relax, the blood flows in and out at the normal rate, and the penis goes back to being limp.

Foreskin: All boys are born with a thick fold of skin which covers the penis. This is the foreskin and it's the equivalent to the hood of skin that protects the clitoris. The foreskin usually covers the head of the penis but it can be drawn back over the shaft. Under the foreskin a whitish waxy secretion called smegma – sometimes known as cock-cheese – is produced.

Circumcision is a minor operation which removes the foreskin. The most common difference between penises is whether or not this foreskin has been removed. Some boys are circumcised eight days after they're born; Moslem boys are circumcised when they're eight or older. Baby boys may also be circumcised because many doctors and parents believe that a circumcised penis is easier to keep clean and less likely to get an infection, which the smegma can sometimes cause (see also page 97).

Circumcision makes no difference to a boy's sexual performance. In fact, when a penis is erect it's very difficult to tell whether it's been circumcised or not.

Despite all fears, rumours (and boasts!) to the contrary most penises are the same size: usually about 2 or 3 inches when limp and about 6 inches when erect. But, like all averages, some are a bit smaller and others a bit larger. Boys (and men) can spend a lot of time worrying that their penis is too small

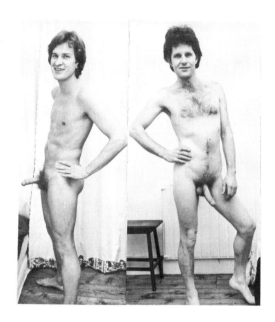

All penises are roughly the same size and shape.
The one on the left is circumcised, the one on
the right is uncircumcised, but when they're
erect it's difficult to tell the difference.

or too thin; although there's really no need. The first thing to remember is that the penis is very sensitive to temperature and to how a boy feels. It may be that a boy who is convinced he has the smallest penis in the world has only been able to compare sizes at times when his fears are making his penis small, and the other boys around having been feeling warm and relaxed and so have a bigger looking penis. And in any case, a penis that is small when it's limp can grow when erect to be as big or bigger than one that is large when it's limp.

One thing is certain: there's nothing anyone can do to increase the size of their penis. Manufacturers who advertise potions and machines which are supposed to make the penis bigger are, for a start, lying. They're just getting rich by playing on the fears of boys and men who think that girls prefer a big penis, and that they are in some way less 'manly' if theirs is small. It's all rubbish – the size of a penis need make no difference to anyone's sexual pleasure.

Testicles: Usually called balls, but other slang words include bollocks, pills, pillocks, nuts, cobblers, and stones. Under the penis is a bag of crinkly dark pink or reddish skin which contains two testicles. This bag is called the

12

scrotum or scrotal sac. One testicle generally hangs down lower than the other – often the left one. They can be hurt easily if squeezed too hard or knocked (which is why cricketers and other sportsmen wear protective boxes over their sex organs). Like the penis, testicles react to temperature and mood. When a boy is relaxed and warm his balls hang loosely. If he's nervous, cold or sexually excited they pull up close to his body.

Pubic hair: Or pubes. This grows round a boy's sex organs and on his balls. It's often a darker colour than the hair that grows on his head.

The inner sex organs

The hormones which change the shape and look of our bodies and outer sex organs also trigger off changes to our internal sex organs inside our bodies. Once our internal sex organs – or reproductive organs – are mature it means we are physically capable of having babies. When a girl reaches sexual maturity a ripe egg cell, called an ovum, is produced in her ovary. The first sign that this has happened is when she has her first period. When a boy reaches sexual maturity sperm is produced in his testicles. The first sign of this is when he has his first ejaculation of a fluid called semen (pronounced see-men),which contains millions of tiny sperm cells. The egg cell and the sperm cell are the two halves of human reproduction. Together the egg and sperm reproduce another human being – in other words, they make a baby.

Reproductive organs – girls

Ovaries: Girls are born with two ovaries. They're made up of millions of tiny follicles which all have an unripe egg cell inside. By the time a girl is physically mature, her ovaries are roughly the size and shape of an unshelled almond.

When she reaches puberty, her ovaries start to produce female sex hormones. These hormones do two things: they make the inner walls of her womb start to thicken with a rich lining of membrane and blood, and they make an egg cell in one of her ovaries start to ripen. Very occasionally two egg cells are produced at the same time (the plural of ovum is ova).

Under the influence of the hormones, a follicle with its ripening egg cells starts to move towards the surface of one or other ovary. When it's ripe, this follicle is released from its ovary. This is called ovulation. Some girls can tell when it's happening because they get a sudden sharp feeling of cramp in the lower part of their abdomen on whichever side the follicle is being released.

When the follicle with its ripe egg pops off from its ovary, it is trapped in the end of the nearest Fallopian tube.

Fallopian tubes: These two tubes are about three inches long. One end comes out of the top of the womb, the other end, which is fringed and funnel-shaped, wraps part way round an ovary. It is in the Fallopian tubes that a baby will be conceived if a sperm cell meets and fertilises an egg cell.

13

When the follicle is trapped by the funnel-shaped fringed end of a Fallopian tube, it separates from the ripe egg cell. The follicle starts to disintegrate and is then called the yellow body because it turns a yellowish colour. The ripe egg and yellow body travel down the Fallopian tube separately. They take about six and a half days to reach the womb.

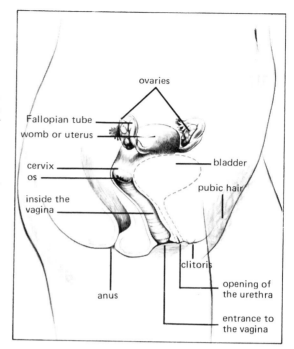

Womb: In a physically mature girl, the womb is about the size of a smallish clenched fist. It has thick walls of muscle, that lie pressed against each other, rather like a balloon without any air in it. While the egg has been travelling down the Fallopian tube, the walls of the womb have been developing a thick lining of membrane and blood. If the egg has been fertilised by a sperm, which means that the girl has become pregnant, it attaches itself to the lining and the growing baby is nourished and fed by this lining.

If the egg has not been fertilised by a sperm, meaning that the girl isn't pregnant, the egg has started to disintegrate by the time it reaches the womb. The already disintegrated yellow body slips out of the womb and a girl may notice it as a yellow stain in her pants. About twelve days after the egg reaches the womb, the muscles in the walls of the womb start to push out its thick lining through the cervix.

Cervix: This is the entrance to the womb. Running through the middle is a small passage called the os. It's about the width of an extremely narrow straw. The lining of the womb is pushed through this passage into the vagina.

Vagina: The vagina is normally about three and a half inches long. It has walls of crinkled or ribbed membrane that normally lie flat against each other. It is a very flexible organ and can stretch to the size of more or less whatever is put in it, such as a finger or tampon, an erect penis or a baby when it is being born. (Which is why the vagina is also called the birth passage).

The womb lining slips out of the vagina, past the hymen if there is one, and a girl has her period. It can take from two to eight days for the womb to push all the lining out.

Periods

The technical word for a period is menstruation. The membrane and blood from the womb is called menstrual blood or flow. The whole process from ovulation to having a period is known as the menstrual cycle. Menstruation comes from the Latin word *menses* which means month – a misleading term because very few women have their periods on a regular monthly or twenty-eight day basis.

Usually by the time a girl is fully sexually mature, her hormones produce another ripe egg in one or other of her ovaries a few days after her period ends and the whole cycle starts all over again. But while her hormones are becoming adjusted, a girl often has to wait several months or perhaps more than a year before she has her next period. Eventually most women have their period every twenty-five to thirty-five days or so. But it's very rare for periods to happen absolutely regularly on the day each time. There are many reasons why a period can be early or late or missed altogether. Pregnancy is one reason, because during pregnancy hormones are produced in her body which prevent any more egg cells from ripening. Other reasons can be ill-health, emotional shock, fear of being pregnant or simply a change in climate or in normal routine.

Periods can last anything from two to eight days. Some girls have very light periods, others have very heavy ones. The normal amount of blood lost is about five or six tablespoons – although because blood spreads and stains it can seem a lot more.

Sanitary towel or tampon?

Sanitary towels or tampons have to be used to absorb the period flow. There are many different brands to choose from. Sanitary towels are pads of absorbent cotton which fit under the entrance to the vagina inside pants or tights. Some have loops at each end to be attached to a belt which fastens round the waist. This sort tend to be rather big and lumpy – impossible to wear with tight trousers. But there are many different brands now which are small and compact and don't show at all even in a bikini. It's worth shopping around for the type which feels most comfortable.

Many girls find tampons are more convenient. These are small finger-like wads of absorbent cotton wool that give internal protection. They are pushed up into the vagina where they expand to absorb the flow and fit comfortably in the vagina.

If a girl's hymen has not been broken, she may find it difficult to push the tampon in. But many hymens have holes in them which makes it possible to do this. If she does break her hymen when she pushes a tampon in, she may feel some pain. But it's often just a quick short sharp pain that quickly goes

15

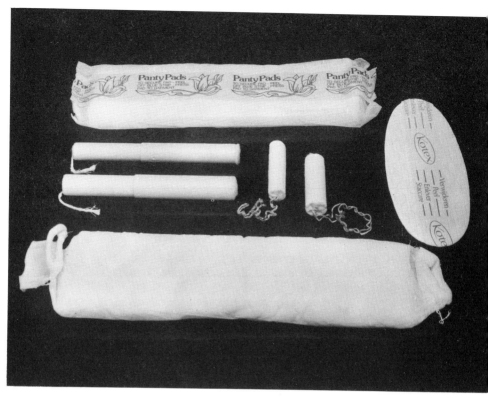

Sanitary towels and tampons. Choose the type that feels the most comfortable. The tampons on the left are in their cardboard applicators which can be flushed away once the tampon has been put into the vagina.

away and it's quite a good way of getting the whole business of hymen-breaking over and done with (see also Virginity on page 45).

If putting a tampon in proves difficult it will be easier to wait until the period is over and then practise with a mirror to find out exactly where it should go. Another tip is to smear it with some sterile lubricating jelly, such as KY jelly, that you can buy over the counter at a chemists. This will help to slide it in more easily.

Pulling them out can sometimes cause problems. Each one has a small string attached to the end which hangs down outside the vagina. The best way to pull them out is to squat or stand with one leg raised on a chair or side of the bath, relax and give the string a gentle tug. If the string can't be found or the tampon seems to be stuck, it won't do any harm to wriggle a couple of fingers inside the vagina to find it and pull it out. If it's still stuck, don't panic. But don't leave it in either — it could cause an infection. If you can't ask a friend or your mother to help you, go to your doctor and ask her or him to pull it out. This may sound like a drastic measure but doctors are often asked to do this.

Tampons come in different sizes – find one that feels most comfortable. One brand, called Tampax, has cardboard applicators to help put them in. The tampon is pushed out of its applicator into the vagina and you then throw the cardboard tube away.

Sanitary towels and tampons have to be changed regularly – several times a day is best and more often if the period is very heavy. Menstrual blood doesn't smell until it reaches the air when it can start to smell quite unpleasant – so it's a good idea to change towels or tampons perhaps four or five times a day.

One of the best things about tampons is that they can be flushed down the toilet. Some sanitary towels are supposedly disposable in this way, but they often clog up the toilets.

Most towels have to be wrapped up and put in the dustbin or on the fire. Towels and tampons work out fairly expensive so some girls like to use a small bit of sponge with a little string attached. This can then be washed out and used again and again.

What it feels like to have a period

Her first period can be a big event in a girl's life. It's proof that her body is maturing and that she'll be able to have babies if she wants to. But it can be a frightening experience, especially if no one has explained what is happening to her body.

Few people find it easy to talk openly about periods. Perhaps that's why so many slang words are used. It's often called being on the rag, on drip, feeling poorly, jam butties, aunty, monthlies, the time of the month, holy week, the curse and many other names. In the past there have been times when a woman who was having her period was thought to have magical powers. But more often than not she's been made to feel dirty, unclean or unlucky. Most unfairly, menstruating women have been accused of ruining crops, causing calves to be born dead and preventing the bread from rising. Small wonder it came to be called the curse!

There's still a lot of taboo surrounding the subject. Until very recently sanitary towels were rarely advertised and shops kept them well hidden from view. Many boys and men find the thought of periods so repulsive that they won't have sex with someone who is having her period and are often too embarrassed to buy towels or tampons for her in the chemists. Girls who feel ill when they have their periods seldom like to say why they're feeling rotten.

There's no reason why someone who is having her period shouldn't have sex if she wants to – in fact it often helps relieve the pain of cramps to have orgasms and having a period is nothing to feel ashamed about. Perhaps if more people stopped to think why women have periods they wouldn't feel so shy or upset by the thought of them.

Having periods affects everyone in different ways. Some girls barely notice when they're having one. Others can feel grumpy, irritable or get a lot of pain. There are different sorts of pains that periods can cause. Some girls suffer from a constant dragging pain that can start several days before the period begins, called pre-menstrual tension, and some get sharper attacks of cramp-like pains actually during the period. Girls with irregular periods often suffer in particular from these pains (see also page 98). The pains often disappear as a girl gets older and her periods become more regular. What a girl needs if she's suffering from pains or if her period is making her feel low is not for everyone around her to feel embarassed or repulsed, or even necessarily to ignore what's happening to her body, but to understand why she's feeling the way she is. There's no denying that periods can be a bit messy and sometimes inconvenient or painful. But they're a very natural part of being female.

Reproductive organs – boys

Testicles: Inside the scrotum or scrotal sac there are two glands called testes (pronounced test-ees) or testicles. Both of these are divided into several chambers which contain some very long, narrow, twisted tubes. When a boy reaches puberty the male sex hormone which is produced inside his testicles starts to cause sperm cells to be made inside these long narrow tubes. When the sperms have been made they pass out of each testicle into an epididymis (pronounced eppy-did-eye-miss).

Epididymis: These organs lie on top of each testicle. They are made up of masses of larger tubes. Sperms are stored in each epididymis until a boy starts to get sexually excited and his penis grows erect. They are then pushed out of each epididymis by an automatic relaxing/contracting movement (a bit like swallowing) of the tubes into two seminal ducts.

Seminal ducts: These are two narrow tubes, technically known as the vas deferens, which go from each epididymis to a prostate gland. The sperms are pushed up the seminal ducts to this gland.

Prostate glands: This gland is inside the lower part of a boy's abdomen. It produces a fluid called seminal fluid. The sperms mix with this fluid and the mixture then passes out of the prostate gland into the seminal vesicles (pronounced vees-ickels).

Seminal Vesicles: These are two small areas or sacs which store the sperm and seminal fluid mixture, which is called semen, until a boy reaches the peak of sexual excitement. At this point it leaves the vesicles and goes into a single tube called the urethra.

Urethra: This tube runs through the middle of the penis. The semen rushes through the urethra and comes out of the tip of the penis in four or five spurts. This is called ejaculation.

Inside a boy's body, at the point where the urethra joins the seminal vesicles, the urethra branches into two smaller tubes. One of these, as described above, goes to the inner sex organs. The other branch goes up to the bladder where pee collects. There is a tiny valve in the urethra tubes

18

The sex organs of a boy showing the internal reproductive organs

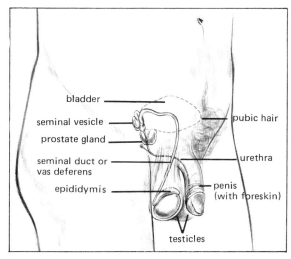

bladder

seminal vesicle

prostate gland

seminal duct or vas deferens

epididymis

pubic hair

urethra

penis (with foreskin)

testicles

which means that when pee comes out of the bladder it bypasses the seminal vesicles, and carries on down through the penis and out of the hole in the tip. This valve makes sure that a boy can't pee and ejaculate at the same time.

When the penis is limp the valve opens the tube to the bladder. As soon as the penis starts to go erect, the valve closes the tube to the bladder and opens the tube to the sex organs.

Semen: Also called spunk, sex fluid, jism. Although there are about 300 million sperms in the average amount of semen ejaculated, they only form a very small portion of it. The bulk of it consists of the seminal fluid. The sperms are microscopic – you couldn't tell the difference in the look or amount of semen if all 300 millions were removed. Once a boy reaches sexual maturity, his testicles are constantly producing new sperms. There's no possibility of using them all up. If a boy has several ejaculations in a day, the amount of sperm and fluid will be slightly reduced – but there will still be many millions of sperm in each ejaculation for the rest of his life.

Semen is a milky, sticky, thickish liquid. It has a slightly salty, almost bitter taste. It's not poisonous. It can stain material if left – it soon hardens – but it's easy to wash off with soap and water.

Ejaculating: also called shooting your load, coming. Most boys start to ejaculate by the age of about 12. But some start earlier and others later. It all depends on when those hormones cause sperms to be produced.

Just as a girl's first period can happen without warning, so can a boy's first ejaculation. He may wake up one morning to discover semen on his pyjamas, not having known anything about it when it happened. (He may think that he's peed in his sleep). When this happens it's called having a wet dream or a nocturnal emission. Or he may be feeling his penis, as he perhaps has throughout childhood, when semen suddenly spurts out. Having an erection doesn't mean a boy will automatically ejaculate – but he can't ejaculate unless he's got an erection. The time it takes from erection to ejaculation can vary. It can take a few seconds or it can take several minutes or longer.

Erection: Also called having a hard on, on the bonk, feeling horny. Getting an erection is usually, but not always, the result of some kind of sexy or erotic influence. It happens quite naturally, a bit like blushing. Many boys after the age of eleven or so find that they get erections for no obvious reason at all and sometimes many a day. It can happen in the gym, on the top of a bus, at the breakfast table – and by just wondering when it will happen. This is quite natural, and sudden, unexpected and often unwanted erections stop happening after a time. But it can be embarrassing. An erection isn't always the easiest thing in the world to hide. The best thing to do is to try thinking about something else entirely. Concentrating on your kid brother or your homework can do wonders to make your penis shrink. Having an erection is a perfectly normal thing but you might get a bit of a pain or ache in your balls and the lower part of your stomach after a while. Having an ejaculation often helps to ease this pain.

Wet Dreams

Both girls and boys have wet dreams (or dreams in which they reach a peak of sexual excitement) but girls don't ejaculate. The sort of dream that makes a boy ejaculate is often very sexy. It's quite natural for a boy to dream about having sex with someone he knows well of the same or opposite sex even though in the daytime he mightn't think about them in a sexy way at all. Or he may dream about someone of either sex whom he fancies. The dreams may involve violent situations. No one has yet found a way of controlling our dreams and hopefully they never will. And however violent or odd a dream may be, having it doesn't mean that you're automatically going to grow up to be a rapist or to be hopelessly in love with your brother or mother!

Many boys hate waking up to find semen all over their pyjamas and sheets. If you want to avoid this, try sleeping in underpants which can then be washed out the next morning, or give yourself an ejaculation before you go to sleep, and use a paper handkerchief to absorb the semen.

The good thing about having a wet dream and ejaculating is that it's a sure sign of reaching sexual maturity, just as periods are for a girl. But not every boy has them. He may only ejaculate when he masturbates or he may never ejaculate until he has sex. Most men ejaculate at some time in their lives, but if they don't, the sperms just disintegrate, and are absorbed into the body without causing any harm.

Egg and sperm together: fertilisation

A girl can only get pregnant if a ripe egg cell in her Fallopian tubes is fertilised by a sperm cell.

When a couple have sexual intercourse the man puts his erect penis into a woman's vagina (see page 41). When he ejaculates the millions of sperms in his semen swim blindly around in the vagina, up through the small passage (the os) in the entrance to the womb (cervix) and into the womb (uterus).

Conception: a greatly enlarged diagram of a sperm entering an egg. Out of the many millions of sperms in the semen it takes only one to fertilise the egg. Once this has happened, a baby is conceived and the fertilised egg travels down the Fallopian tube and attaches itself to the wall of the womb.

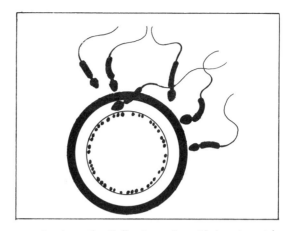

From the womb, sperms swim into the Fallopian tubes. If there's a ripe egg cell in one of the Fallopian tubes, a sperm may enter and fertilise it. It's at this point that a baby is conceived. If, as occasionally happens, a fertilised egg splits into two, identical twins will be produced. Sometimes two ripe egg cells develop at the same time; if they are both fertilised, non-identical twins will be the result.

Another way in which women can get pregnant is by having some sperms inserted into their womb scientifically by a doctor. It's been discovered that sperms can be kept alive and unharmed for several years by freezing them. The sperms can then be used by women who haven't been able to get pregnant by a man who is infertile (which means that his body doesn't produce sperms). Lesbian women, women who don't want to have sex with a man because they feel sexually attracted to women rather than men, can also have babies in this way. Several sperm banks have been set up for these purposes, and it's called having a child by AID which stands for Artificial Insemination by Donor. (Insemination just means sowing).

Who am I ?

The sex organs of all girls look roughly alike. So do the sex organs of boys. But it must be obvious that just as no two people develop at exactly the same time or in the same way, no two people are ever exactly alike sexually. But the society we live in tries to make us feel we should belong to clearly labelled categories. People tend to judge each other by what society as a whole seems to think of as 'normal'. According to society it's 'normal' for girls and boys to be sexual opposites. Girls are taught to be soft and passive towards boys and boys are brought up to think they have to be tough and aggressive towards girls.

In our society, many people think it's 'unfeminine' for a girl to ask a boy out for a date or to admit that she enjoys sex. And it's considered 'unmasculine' for a boy to enjoy ballet or let his girlfriend order a round of drinks in a pub. Treating girls and boys differently like this is called having double standards. And expecting everyone to act in a certain way because of their sex when maybe they don't feel like acting this way can make people unhappy.

A boy, for example, is often almost expected to sleep around a bit, and be a 'bit of a lad' with as many girls as he can while he's young. Girls, on the other hand, are expected to 'save themselves' for the man they marry. Boys are often allowed to stay out late and many people tend to turn a blind eye if they smoke or drink beer when they're quite young. Girls find that they're expected to stay at home – often to babysit – or at least be in early, and sip only the occasional Babycham. You can see how unfair these sort of stereotypes are for girls and boys who don't quite fit the picture of what makes a so called 'perfect' girl or boy. Girls find that they're thought to be slightly odd or masculine if they want to play football, or be an engineer when they leave school. Boys are accused of being 'sissy' if they cry when they're sad, or want to be a nurse.

Society's view of what it means to be female or male also affects how we're all supposed to think about sex. It's assumed to be automatic and normal for women and men to be sexually attracted to each other. This is true for the majority of people – that's to say, most people are heterosexual.

But it isn't true for everyone. Some people, homosexuals, are attracted to the same sex. Bisexuals are attracted to both sexes. And some people who are asexual aren't attracted by anyone and choose to live without a sex life. Just because they're not in the majority, it doesn't mean that these people are not normal or that their sex lives are 'unnatural'.

There have been lots of theories as to why some of us are heterosexual while others are homosexual, bisexual, or asexual, but none of them have ever been very satisfactory. The chemical make-up of our bodies may have something to do with it. But there are no hard and fast rules. It's no good thinking that because someone had a very powerful mother and a weak father that they'll turn out automatically to be homosexual. This may happen or it may not.

In some societies there have been times when it was totally acceptable for people to be homosexual or bisexual, and there are still those who find it a completely acceptable way to live. But in the western world today, being anything other than heterosexual is not easy because our society tends to treat everyone who isn't as abnormal. Many homosexuals now call themselves gays – not because they're always happy, but because they're content to have discovered this about themselves, and they know that it's nothing to be ashamed of. But non-gays (often called straights) go on calling them queers, lezzies, dykes, poufs, poufters, pansies, fairies, queens, faggots and countless other cruel and insulting names. Not only do they get called hurtful names, but people also treat them in hurtful ways.

How we enjoy sex should be a matter of individual sexual preference. There's no reason to believe that if any one of us landed on a desert island, with only another member of the same sex, we might not find it easy and natural to have a homosexual relationship. Many people if left to their own natural instincts might find they were bisexual and could enjoy relationships with women and men. But society tries to make us hold back these instincts. This can make it very difficult for some people to find out what their sexual tastes are. Holding back a natural sexual feeling can make people feel bewildered and very unhappy.

Neither heterosexuality nor homosexuality is some sort of dangerous drug that you get hooked on to for the rest of your life – which is what some people would have us believe. A very large number of women and men who would not think of themselves as gay have had some kind of homosexual experience at some time in their lives. Some girls and boys experiment with their own sex before they brave a relationship with the opposite sex. Certainly around puberty many of us go through a time when we don't have a lot of time for the opposite sex and get strong sexual feelings for people of the same sex. If we have sexual experiences with the same sex it isn't going to harm us any more than if we have sexual experiences with the opposite sex and in the end find out we prefer to be gay. The point is to realise that we all have different sexual tastes and to be in a minority doesn't make anyone 'abnormal' or in the wrong.

About one in twenty people in this picture are probably homosexual. There's no section of society which doesn't have its proportion of gays and you can't tell just by looking at someone whether they're gay or not.

Homosexuality

A homosexual is a woman or a man who is sexually attracted to the same sex — a woman who has a sexual preference for women and a man who has a sexual preference for men. The women are called lesbians or gays and the men are called homosexuals or gays.

About one in twenty people are gay — although not all necessarily discover this about themselves immediately. This figure means that there are about two million homosexuals of both sexes in the UK.

According to the way society likes to put everyone into clearly labelled boxes, all homosexual men are supposed to have limp wrists, squeaky voices, rounded hips and act 'like women' (however it is that women are supposed to act!). All lesbians are supposed to be tough with gruff voices, short-back-and-sides hair-dos, and to dress and act like men. How wrong can you get! Of course some gays live up to this picture — just as some straight women and men live up to what is called a stereotyped picture. But the way people look or dress doesn't have to have anything to do with how they enjoy sex. Business women and men, factory workers, pop stars, politicians, teachers, Lords of the Realm – there's no section of society that doesn't have its proportion of homosexuals. But because some sections of society have tended to treat gays better than others, many gays have doubtless been attracted to the sort of jobs where they will find fellow workers who won't treat them as freaks.

Sexually, gays have the same sort of relationships as heterosexuals. They may have sex for fun, out of curiosity, for friendship or for love. They give and get sexual pleasure and satisfaction by kissing, cuddling, feeling and stimulating other's sex organs with their hands and mouths just like non-gays. Some, but not all, male gays have anal intercourse (which means putting the penis into the anus) just as some heterosexual couples do. For homosexuals, sex is as natural as it is for everyone else. What they do and how they give and get sexual pleasure is up to them as individuals.

In the past homosexual men have been treated very inhumanely. Until 1969, homosexuality was actually illegal in England – and still is in Scotland, Northern Ireland and Eire. Lesbianism has never been illegal – but it's never been easy for gay women to admit their love for each other publicly. It is still impossible for gays to marry and only very recently have gay women been allowed to adopt children or to have babies by artificial insemination. Gay men still have to fight for the right to adopt children. Many people believe that gay men tend to sleep around a lot and change their partners as often as the weather. This could be one reason why society frowns on the idea of allowing gays to get married or adopt children. But as the divorce laws make it easier for unhappy heterosexuals to split up and as homosexuals find it easier to be open about their relationships this belief is becoming exposed for the myth that it is. There are plenty of female and male homosexual relationships which last either a lifetime or for many years. Some are shorter, but these variations exist in heterosexual relationships as well. Attitudes are slowly changing for the better but there are still far too many people who treat gays as disgusting perverts who deserve prison sentences, or as ill and in need of a 'cure'.

Gays are finding it easier to be open about their sexual preference for the same sex – but for many it still causes problems. Some gays for instance can feel so hung up about their particular sexual preference that they get married to non-gays in the hope that this will 'cure' them. They often end up in a position of being hurt, even more scared, and hurting the person they married. Homosexuality isn't an illness – it's simply a matter of a sex instinct that is directed to the same sex.

Discovering that you are or might be gay can come as something of a shock. Society, after all, has been impressing on you that to be gay is to be abnormal. The legal position for gays is explained on page 104. If you are gay or think you might be and want legal help, moral support or advice, contact one of the organisations mentioned on pages 118-120.

Bisexuality

A bisexual is someone who is attracted to both sexes and who enjoys sex with women and men. Bisexuals might fall in love and choose to live with someone of either sex. Many people, if they're honest, feel attracted to someone of the same sex at some time or other – although not everyone is always prepared to admit this even to themselves. But not everyone, whether gay, straight or bisexual wants to have sex with everyone they're attracted to.

People who find out or think they may be bisexual often feel very frightened because it's as if they don't fit into any particular category and so may be rejected by everyone. But there are no such things as clearly defined categories and no one should be made to feel as if they have to live in a labelled box.

If you are or think you may be bisexual and want legal help, moral support or advice, contact one of the organisations on page 118-120.

Masturbation

There are countless words for masturbating: wanking, fiddling, playing with yourself, jacking off, jerking off, tossing off, bringing yourself off are just some of them.

Very simply, masturbating means rubbing your clitoris or penis – usually, though not always, with your hand – in order to get sexually excited and often (though again not always) give yourself an orgasm. It gives you a good feeling and it's a way of getting to know how your body works and responds to sexual excitement.

There's a full description of what having an orgasm means on page 32 but in simple terms it's this: by rubbing her clitoris a girl gets sexually excited. As she reaches the peak of excitement her whole body feels in tune with the sensations in her sex organs. Unlike a boy, she doesn't produce any fluid that spurts out but her vagina does produce a fluid when she's aroused, before her orgasm, which makes her sex organs wet. When she reaches the peak or climax of sexual pleasure the muscles in her vagina start to move in spasms and the feelings of tenseness and excitement mingle with a feeling of release and satisfaction.

A boy gets much the same sensations from rubbing his penis. The movement gives him an erection and he reaches a peak of sexual excitement. This feeling spreads from his sex organs to the whole of his body. At the climax, semen comes out of the hole in the tip of his penis, in four or five spurts. The feeling of tenseness and excitement mixes into a feeling of release and satisfaction. His penis goes limp almost immediately afterwards and his body goes back to being relaxed.

The slang expressions for having an orgasm, such as coming, arriving or getting there, are quite good descriptions for what it can feel like.

The myths
Doctors have known for years that masturbating is totally harmless, but many people still have the suspicion lurking in the back of their minds that it's a

27

dangerous or even wicked thing to do. Many of the jokes and limericks about wanking reflect this suspicion:

> There was a young man named Hank
> Who often enjoyed a good wank
> But he once gave a cough
> And his penis dropped off
> To be frank, Hank regrets learning to wank.

Most of us have heard at some time or other that masturbating can:

- make you blind
- drive you mad
- make you sterile and unable to have babies
- ruin a marriage
- dry up the brain
- alter the shape of your sex organs
- drain the 'vital juices'
- give you spots
- give you cancer
- give you stomach aches
- give you headaches

But NONE of these things are true. There's absolutely NO evidence of any kind at all of a connection between masturbating and madness or any illness.

There was a young lady named . . .

There's another myth about masturbating which suggests that it's not something girls do. It is true that many more boys do it than girls but the reason for this is not because girls don't have sexual feelings but because of the difference in their bodies and the different ways in which they're brought up sexually. Many boys, even in this day and age, are discouraged from masturbating, but parents can't tell their sons not to touch their penis or they wouldn't be able to pee. But parents often firmly discourage their daughters from playing with their sex organs. Some girls are told outright lies, like their sex organs will drop off if they touch themselves. This means that girls, even more than boys, grow up thinking that to feel themselves is somehow 'naughty' or 'wrong' or in some way dangerous. Of course some girls go right ahead and learn how to masturbate, and others teach themselves when they're much older. But some don't, and many tend to feel very guilty about getting good sexual feelings from masturbating. And this feeling of guilt can spread to their whole attitude towards all sex.

Women and girls of all ages enjoy masturbating every bit as much as men and boys. Masturbating can't harm anyone, so no one should feel guilty or scared about it.

So why all the myths?

In the past the most dreadful punishments were handed out to girls and boys found masturbating. Up to the nineteenth century they might have had their arms bound to their sides in splints, their thighs blistered with hot irons, some boys were circumcised (although this never stopped any boy from wanking) and some girls had their clitoris removed. Some unfortunate men in mental hospitals who were often thought by the authorities to masturbate 'too much' had their penis chopped off altogether.

The main reason for all this was that many people were convinced that sex was wrong unless it took place between a married couple who wanted to have a baby. This was certainly the opinion of most religious people, who could find passages from the Bible to support their view. It's easy to see why masturbation, which obviously can't get anyone pregnant, came to be thought of as sinful and unnatural.

Attitudes like this die hard. For some religious and more traditionally-minded people the feeling that masturbating is wrong or immoral lives on. Your parents, teachers or doctors may have been brought up along these lines and may still think like this.

If your own moral sense or religious beliefs tell you that sex *is* only for having babies or you want to conform to your parents point of view, and they think it's wrong, then masturbating may not be for you. There's no sense in doing anything that you strongly believe to be wrong. But if you do masturbate and enjoy the feelings you get, don't worry that it will make you ill or damage you in any way. It won't.

How girls masturbate

There isn't any one, or a right or wrong, way in which to masturbate. There are so many different ways that it's impossible to mention them all but the majority of girls use a finger, several fingers or their whole hand to rub gently and rhythmically over the clitoris until they reach orgasm. Or they may use a firmer action over the whole vaginal area, perhaps using both hands for greater pressure. The action usually gets faster and faster until they come.

Rubbing against a dry clitoris can sometimes make it feel a bit sore, so use some of the wetness produced inside the vagina, some spit or something gentle like KY Jelly that you can buy from the chemist.

A few find that they can bring themselves off by using the muscles in their vagina. This usually needs a bit of practice — if you don't know where these muscles are or how to make them contract you can try the following exercise: when you're peeing, tighten the muscles in your vaginal area to hold back the pee for a little while. When you've found out where these muscles are you can practise making them contract and relax any time during the day — no one will notice what you're doing.

Another way of masturbating is to use a sheet, pillow or flannel and pull it back and forwards over the clitoris. Some like to put a finger or two in their vagina or anus because at the peak of an orgasm the muscles in both these organs contract in spasms. Spraying the clitoris and vagina with a jet of water can also give an orgasm. Some girls have learned how to come in this way because they were told never to touch themselves and so always washed their vaginas under the tap or used a shower spray. You may find you have an orgasm by touching your nipples, or your clitoris and a nipple at the same time, or by crossing your legs and rubbing them together.

Some women masturbate with sex toys. Vibrators and dildoes (sometimes called dildols) are penis-shaped objects made of rubber or plastic. Vibrators are powered by batteries or can be plugged into the electricity to make them shake or vibrate slightly. They are used to play gently over the clitoris and sex organs or put inside the vagina. These sex toys often cost a lot of money and there are many much cheaper things around the house which do just as well. Obviously nothing should be used that might irritate or harm the tender skin of the sex organs. But no one should feel guilty because they like to use something other than their fingers.

How long it takes to masturbate can vary. Much depends on how long it takes to get in the right mood — this can take a minute or two or it can take up to an hour or more. Many girls find that it takes them a long time to learn how to masturbate and reach an orgasm. But whether or not they come, most girls find it enjoyable and exciting.

How boys masturbate

One way is to make a fist, hold the penis quite firmly in it and jerk the hand up and down with a shaking action that gets faster and faster as the excitement builds up. A boy who hasn't been circumcised likes to bring the foreskin up and down over the head of the penis. Some boys prefer a less vigorous method and they stroke the head of the penis with their finger tips. Or they may masturbate without using their hands at all by lying on their stomachs and pushing their bodies up and down to make their penis rub against the bed or ground.

Some boys find that it increases their pleasure to push a finger up their anus. It isn't a good idea to push anything inside the penis because of the danger of harming the delicate tissue inside or of getting an infection.

Some boys like to put the inner cardboard tube from a toilet-paper roll on their penis. Or they use butter, oil or soapy water to make the penis feel nice and slippery. There's probably nothing that hasn't been used by someone at some time or other. It occurs to most boys to try to suck their penis — although most find this best left to india-rubber men!

Can masturbating do any good?

It can certainly relieve tension. Many sports people are discouraged from masturbating before a game or a race. This is probably all part of the old-fashioned view that masturbating is bad for you and weakens your body by draining it of its 'vital juices' (whatever they might be). Some athletes say they've given their best record-breaking performances after they've had an orgasm. It all depends on whether you're the sort of person who needs to be tense before a performance or prefers to feel relaxed. The amount of energy you use up when you masturbate is probably about the same as walking up a flight of stairs — and no athlete has ever been told to stay at ground level before a race.

Another thing in favour of masturbating is that it helps you to get to know your own body. It needn't be just a mechanical means of relieving tension, like peeing is a mechanical means of emptying your bladder. It's a way of enjoying sex on your own if you can't or don't want to have sex with someone else.

30

Masturbating can also take your mind off any problems you may have. This is why some people with worries and problems masturbate a lot. You can't masturbate 'too much', but wanking doesn't solve your problems. And if you spend most of your time doing nothing but masturbating and thinking about it you'll never get round to finding any solutions.

Masturbating is usually a very private thing, although some girls and boys sometimes get a kick out of doing it in a group. If that's how you enjoy it, there's nothing wrong in sharing sex in this way. If, as most people do, you prefer wanking in private, the big fear can be that you'll be discovered by your parents or by someone whom you don't want to know. If you should be interrupted, and whoever it is that disturbs you looks horrified, try to figure out why they're horrified. It could well be that they disapprove altogether, in which case you'll have to find a more private place in future. Or it could be simply that *they're* upset that *you* might be upset to be discovered doing something you wanted to do in private.

Enjoying a good wank can be very pleasurable – many women say that the orgasm they get from masturbating is more intense than when they reach orgasm through sexual intercourse. Some people masturbate because they're frightened of having a relationship with someone else. But no one should worry that just because they masturbate they'll never fully enjoy sex with a partner. Every single sexual experience whether with a partner or on your own is different each and every time. Ignore the myth that suggests that if you masturbate and enjoy it you'll never be able to have a good sexual relationship with another person – this simply isn't true.

Some people think of masturbation as a poor substitute for having sex with someone else. Perhaps that's why someone who mucks around and never gets down to the real thing in life is often called 'a wanker'. But wanking and coming can make people feel very good. And it is a way of getting sexual pleasure and satisfaction and learning how to love your body.

Finally: You don't *have* to masturbate if you don't want to. Some girls and boys never feel the need. This doesn't mean that you're never going to enjoy sex. Different people have different needs at various times and ages. No one should feel that they must have sex just because they think everyone else is having it. Only you will be able to tell whether you want it, and when and how you want it.

Orgasms

Slang words for having an orgasm and the peak or climax of an orgasm are mostly connected with travelling – they include coming or having a come, getting there, arriving and making it. You can have an orgasm either by masturbating or by having sex with someone else.

Having an orgasm follows a similar physical pattern for both girls and boys, although the feelings and sensation often differ, both from time to time, and from person to person. First of all we get aroused and our bodies start to feel ready for sex. Sexual excitement builds up to a high level, and, at the peak, the sex organs contract in a series of spasms and a feeling of release and sexual pleasure flows through the whole body.

Most boys know what it's like to have an orgasm before they ever have sex with anyone because masturbating and ejaculating are a normal part of their lives. It's obvious when a boy comes – semen spurts out of the end of his penis. A girl doesn't have such an obvious physical sign and it's less easy to tell when she comes. Writers who have tried to describe the female orgasm tend to go in for some very lurid and flowery writing – waves crashing overhead, thunder and lightning booming and flashing around and the occasional earthquake!

It's very easy to be misled by such over-dramatic descriptions. Some girls can be waiting so intently for the flashes and booms that they either don't have an orgasm or don't realise they've had one when they have. The truth is that all women respond differently and each orgasm can vary in intensity. Sometimes an orgasm can slip out like a quiet happy sigh. At other times it can be a very powerful feeling that shakes the whole body, and totally invades the mind.

For many girls, having an orgasm is something they have to learn by masturbating. If a girl can find out for herself how her body responds and likes to be stimulated, it'll be easier for her to enjoy sex to the full with someone else if and when she wants to because she'll be able to show her sex partner how her particular body works.

Getting turned on

Our bodies need to be turned on (or sexually stimulated and aroused as it's called) in order to start to feel ready for sex. You can get aroused in lots of ways, and direct contact with the penis or clitoris isn't the only way to get excited. Kissing, cuddling, touching, stroking, caressing your own or another's body in any number of places – lips, breasts, back, legs, head, hair or anywhere that feels good – can start to turn you on. Or you may feel aroused by seeing someone you fancy, by looking at sexy books, magazines or films or just having sexy thoughts.

Many people enjoy thinking or fantasizing about sex while they masturbate or have sex with someone. It often helps get you into a sexy mood and reach an orgasm more easily. What you think about when you masturbate can range from imagining or remembering being kissed to going the whole way and having sexual intercourse. To some extent our fantasies come from the kind of world we live in. It's quite natural to fantasize about having sex with someone you know well – a friend, someone in your family, a teacher – with someone of the same or opposite sex, about going with or being a prostitute or about raping someone or being raped. There's no limit to what people can fantasize about and there's no need to be scared about even quite violent fantasies. You might day-dream – or fantasize – about being a pop-star or winning an Olympic Gold Medal, but as long as you don't act like a super-star or expect to be treated as one, then no one is going to think you odd. The same thing applies to sexual fantasies. As long as you don't think you have to act out your wilder sex thoughts, there's nothing to worry about.

Being sexually aroused is a good feeling no matter who or what turns you on. Some people would like to ban all sexy books and films – perhaps because deep down what they're really complaining about is that people enjoy getting sexual feelings. But it's possible to be turned on by listening to classical music or by riding on a bus. No one has yet suggested that Beethoven or public transport should be banned!

Having an orgasm – girls

It used to be thought that the vagina was the centre of a girl's orgasm and that the only way for her to come was to have something in her vagina moving up and down. This helped to make some men – and women – think that unless there was a man around with an erect penis women couldn't enjoy sex. But then it was noticed that most women needed to have their clitoris stimulated in order to come. This led to another myth: that women could have two sorts of orgasms, one in the clitoris and one in the vagina. In fact there is only one kind of orgasm and it involves all the sex organs.

Orgasms feel different for different people and at different times, but there are certain physical changes that happen to their bodies when they come. As she gets sexually aroused and excited her nipples become firm and erect and her breasts swell slightly. In some girls this shows a lot, in others it's barely noticeable. The feelings are passed to her sex organs. The clitoris becomes firm and pokes out of its hood of skin which makes it easier to stimulate. Blood rushes to the sex organs, which go a darker pinky-red colour in much the same way as your face goes red when you blush. The outer lips become firmer and separate from each other. Some girls find that the whole of the front of their bodies including their faces, become warm and flushed.

The vagina reacts to excitement in several ways. The innermost two thirds stretches and the walls of the outer third, just inside the entrance, swell out and secrete a clear or slightly whitish fluid that can leak out and make the whole of the outer sex organs wet. All the muscles in her body tense up and breathing gets faster. Just before the peak or climax the clitoris, still firm, goes back into its hood.

The climax of an orgasm involves a series of short rhythmical spasms in the walls of the outer, third part, of the vagina. These spasms spread up to the womb, to all the sex organs and sometimes to the whole body. The muscles of the anus also usually contract in spasms which is why some people like to put a finger in their anus to add to their pleasure.

Some girls find that before they've quite got over having an orgasm, they can have another one or a series in a row, maybe four or five, with only a few seconds in between. But having a series, or multiple orgasm as it's known, isn't necessarily any better than having one on its own. Most have just the one and that's all they need to feel perfectly satisfied.

All this happens to a girl's body quite naturally when she has an orgasm, whether she's masturbating or having intercourse. With all the talk of red flushes and mind-blowing spasms some girls worry that they look very ugly when they come. Nothing could be further from the truth – when does anyone who is feeling excited and happy ever look anything other than lovely? And anyway it doesn't all happen very noticeably to every girl or every time. It doesn't mean she isn't having an orgasm just because her nipples aren't erect, or because her vagina isn't producing much fluid. It's like blushing – some people go red in the face when they're embarrassed; others don't – it doesn't mean that they're any less embarrassed.

Not having an orgasm

There can be many, many reasons why some women find it difficult or seemingly impossible to have an orgasm. The most common reason is that they haven't had enough stimulation. If a girl practises masturbating she'll eventually be able to figure out for herself the amount of stimulation her body needs, and where and how she likes to be touched. It's not always so easy if someone else is doing the stimulating. Intercourse isn't always the best way for the clitoris to be stimulated. And a boy may be so keen to get his penis into her vagina that he doesn't spend enough time arousing her sexually first.

Other reasons for not coming can include being scared of sex or of getting pregnant – especially if you're not using any birth control method – or it can simply be that you're not in the right mood. It's easy on the whole for a boy to tell when he's in the mood for sex – he gets an erection. But many girls find it difficult to get aroused if they're thinking about whether someone will come into the room or how uncomfortable and cold it is in the back of a car. Nor is it easy if all she's thinking about is whether or not she'll have an orgasm. You've got to feel relaxed and take the time your body needs to really enjoy sex, and to take pleasure in sex whether you are having an orgasm or not.

Some couples feel they're a complete failure if she doesn't 'come' every single time they have sex. Because of this, some girls like to pretend that they've come when they haven't. With a bit of practice, some heavy breathing, a few writhing movements and some appropriate groans, it's not so difficult to fake. And it may seem like the easy way out if you're being asked insistently if you've come. But there's absolutely no point. For a start, it's nothing more than a lie and a dishonest trick. And if you go on faking you may never learn what it takes for you to have an orgasm. It's usually something that each couple has to work out and, if they can, talk over together. If you've been faking then, when you do want to find out together, it's going to be hard to admit that you've been lying for days, weeks, months or maybe years.

It's important to realise that not everyone has an orgasm every time they have sex. This is perfectly normal and there's no reason why it should be seen as a failure. It can sometimes be very frustrating not to come, but sex isn't just about scoring 'comes'. Having fun, feeling close, getting to know each other and finding out how your and your partner's body works is every bit as important.

A girl who finds it difficult or impossible to have an orgasm and is upset or worried about it may find that it helps to talk about it with her friends or with other women. Some towns have women's groups which might help with advice or information. In London there's a pre-orgasmic therapy group to help women learn together how to have orgasms (contact *Spare Rib*).

Although she or he may not be trained in this field and may even be unsympathetic – especially if you're young – your doctor may be able to help you or send you to a specialist in sex problems. It's worth a try. You can also get help from clinics and centres specialising in sex problems (addresses, page 115). Give them a ring and ask if they have any therapists to advise on sex problems and find out if there is a fee. Sex therapists can't promise an automatic 'cure' – but it often helps to realise that there are people around who don't believe all problems have to last for ever.

Having an orgasm – boys

For a boy the first sign of being sexually aroused is usually an erection. As the sexual excitement increases, his balls swell slightly and draw up close to his body. All his muscles become tense and his breathing gets faster. A warm flush may spread over the front of his body and face. His nipples may become erect and his breasts swell slightly. A few drops of clear fluid (which may have some sperms in it) sometimes come out of the end of his penis.

Inside his body, the sperms are travelling from his testicles to where they are stored a while at the base of his penis. When the peak of excitement is reached, he feels as if he can't hold back any longer and the sperm comes rushing out along the tube in the middle of his penis and spurts out of the tip in four or five spasms. The spasms spread to all his sex organs, his anus and sometimes the whole of his body. Almost immediately afterwards his penis and the rest of his body relax back to normal.

Unlike women, men can't have a series of several orgasms in a row. It can take up to several hours before he can have another erection and come again. Usually the younger a boy is the less time it takes. In the space of eight hours some are able to come perhaps six or seven times, others only once or twice. Ignore all claims that a boy has come time after time like some piston engine — he's got to be exaggerating!

Some boys have long-term problems with getting an erection, keeping it up or in ejaculating. Your doctor may be able to help or tell you where to go for help. Check with your nearest family planning clinic or centre if they have any therapists to help with sex problems like this — you may need to make an appointment and there may be a fee (addresses, page 115). No one can expect a sex therapist to find the automatic cure — but maybe all you need is to talk it over with someone who is understanding. Knowing that you're not the only one with problems is often a great help in itself.

Enjoying sex

Sex can be fun. It makes a lot of people very happy. There are two sides to a sexual relationship — what you do and what you feel in your mind. In all relationships it's easy to hurt or to be hurt, but relationships which involve sex can cause a lot more pain than those that don't. The memories of our first sexual experiences can stay with us and affect our attitude towards sex for the rest of our lives.

When we're young, if we have a sex life, we usually have to keep it secret. This can make us feel guilty and ashamed of what are, after all, very natural desires and feelings. Many people grow up with this sense of guilt. They find it hard to talk openly about sex, try to hide the fact that they enjoy getting sexually aroused and they may never enjoy sex to the full. What's worse, they may try to prevent others from enjoying sex or knowing anything about it.

At its best, sex can be a way of getting closer to someone you care about very much, and of letting them know that you care. Then, if there are any problems as a result, you can be sure that you will be able to share them. For instance, if two people care for one another and the girl gets pregnant and doesn't want to be, or one of them catches a serious disease or gets into big trouble at home because their parents find out, there'll be someone to turn to for help and support.

It also helps to know something about what you're doing. The more you know about how to give and get pleasure, the more enjoyable and less frightening sex will become.

In the end, the question of whether or not to have sex comes down to what you think in your own mind. Anyone who tries to use pressure or force on someone else should stop — and think of the harm that they're probably causing.

This chapter describes some of the ways in which we can enjoy our bodies together. If you're not yet ready for sex it tells you what to expect and perhaps look forward to when you are ready. It describes what sex is about for heterosexuals — not because gays and other minority groups aren't important, but simply because more people turn out to be heterosexual.

Although attitudes are changing, it's still very widely believed that girls and boys should play entirely different, and sometimes totally opposing roles when it comes to sex. Girls often think that they're supposed to pretend not to want or enjoy sex in case they get 'a reputation'. Boys often feel that they're supposed to lead the girl further than she wants to and live up to some sort of reputation of being randy and sex-mad. Many parents who were brought up to think along these lines tend to be horrified if they discover that their daughter is having sex, but if they discover their son is, they're more likely to think 'good luck to him'.

Having double standards like this can lead to dishonest and very confusing situations. Some girls think they won't be respected if they allow a boy they're really fond of to touch them. Some boys, out of this feeling of respect, find out about sex with a girl they don't really like, but won't touch or share their feelings with a girl they do like. It can be very hard on girls who have to suppress all their sexual feelings and pretend they don't want sex when they do and on girls who, because they do have a sex life just get labelled as a 'good lay'. And it can be very hard on boys who aren't sure about what to do or whether they want to have any sex at all if they have to pretend to be super-studs.

One of the most important things that has changed attitudes to sexuality, especially for girls and women, is the enormous increase in knowledge and availability of birth control over the past years – particularly from the 1960s onwards. Being able to have sex without fear of getting pregnant has meant that girls can think of sex as something that they can have for pleasure. And this has changed relations between the sexes too.

Whether you want sex and how far you want to go doesn't depend on whether you are female or male, but on how you feel in yourself as an individual. You may have very good reasons for not wanting a sexual relationship or for wanting to draw the line somewhere. But how other people think you should behave shouldn't be important.

Sex without pregnancy

There's no part of our bodies that can't play a part in enjoying sex. Sexual excitement builds up in each person in different ways through touch, smell, taste and sight. Those areas of our bodies that make us feel sexually aroused when they're touched, kissed or stroked are called erogenous zones.

The mouth, lips and tongue of most people are highly erogenous – that's to say kissing can be a turn on. There's all the difference in the world between the sort of quick dry kiss we give an aunt or uncle and what's called a french kiss, when we part our lips and let our tongue play with the teeth and tongue of someone we really like.

Many girls and some boys find it exciting to have their breasts and nipples stroked and kissed. Nipples are very sensitive organs and stand firm and erect when we become sexually aroused. Some people – girls and boys – can have an orgasm just by touching their nipples or by having them touched.

Although the pleasures of cuddling naked are often greatly underestimated, for many, the most powerful feelings come from touching and gently playing with the sex organs. The heads of the clitoris and penis are the most sensitive parts of all because they're so richly supplied with nerve endings.

Not everyone needs to have an orgasm every time they get aroused or have sex, but learning how to give each other a 'come' by petting is a way of enjoying sex if one of you doesn't want to have intercourse, or if you want to be absolutely sure that the girl doesn't get pregnant.

How he can make her come

He can use his finger to bring her to a climax by rubbing her clitoris or the area around it. Some girls like their clitoris to be stroked gently, others prefer quite hard pressure. But it varies from person to person and from time to time. The best way to find out is to ask, or suggest she shows how she likes it.

She may like the boy to give her a 'come' by stimulating the inside of her vagina – known as finger-fucking. The opening to the vagina usually becomes moist and relaxed and he'll find it easy to slide a finger or two gently inside and to move them in and out. It's best to start off slowly and then begin to speed up. It may help if he feels her clitoris or the area around it with his other fingers – or she may prefer to do this herself.

After she's come, her clitoris may feel very sensitive and almost too painful to be touched any more. But this doesn't necessarily mean that she's come as much as she wants. She may have several orgasms in a row and the third or fourth may be the best one of all. She may like him to go on rubbing her clitoris, or she may be perfectly satisfied and feel that she's come enough.

How she can make him come

There are several ways she can give him his orgasm. She can hold his penis gently but firmly with her fingers or in her fist and them move her hand up and down in much the same way that many boys masturbate. He may like to put his penis in her arm pit while she holds her arm down to her side. Or he can sit astride her and rub his penis up and down between her breasts, which either partner can press together. It's not a good idea for him to rub his penis against her vagina or between her closed thighs as there's a real danger that when he comes some sperm which can survive up to 72 hours on the skin will find their way into her vagina, and make her pregnant.

Oral Sex

Oral sex means using your mouth to enjoy sex by sucking and kissing each others' sex organs. Slang words and expressions for doing this include giving head, a blow job, and going down.

The tastes and smell of our bodies – especially of our sex organs – can be very exciting, although not everyone realises this and many people are a bit scared of what they taste and smell like. Undoubtedly, if someone doesn't wash regularly, licking and kissing their sex organs can be bad news – just as bad breath doesn't make a kiss all that wonderful.

There are manufacturers who take advantage of the shyness many of us feel about how we smell. Adverts encourage us to drown our bodies with perfumes and deodorants. Some girls get to feel that they're not properly dressed until they've used their vaginal or underarm deodorant. Vaginal deodorants can in fact cause infections in the vagina and be positively harmful. But in any case, smelling like a plastic geranium isn't much of a turn-on – except maybe to another plastic geranium. And nothing can be more of a turn-off than getting a mouthful of what tastes like disinfectant. All that's needed is regular washing – water comes a lot cheaper than aerosol cans.

In oral sex, he kneels down between her legs and feels her clitoris with his tongue. By licking and gently nibbling her clitoris, and maybe poking his tongue into her vagina, he can give her an orgasm. The technical term for this is cunnilingus.

When she goes down on him and gives him an orgasm by licking or sucking his penis it's known as fellatio (pronounced fell-art-io). There's nothing dangerous or poisonous about getting semen in your mouth or swallowing it if you want to. In fact, if she jerks her head back just as the semen spurts out it can be very unsatisfying for him. There's no way in which she can get pregnant by getting sperm in her mouth.

When a couple bring each other off together in this way, with her lying on top of him and sucking his penis while he sucks her vagina it's called position 69 – presumably because that's what it looks like – or the French for sixty nine *soixante neuf* (although it certainly isn't something that only French couples do). A warning here: it's a bad idea for her to lie underneath him because she can choke on his semen.

More ways of enjoying sex

By experimenting, most couples can find out just what they like to do with each other. It may take time to find out and it's easy to be a bit clumsy and unsure at first. Some couples enjoy putting a finger up each others' anus. This can hurt a bit unless the finger is well lubricated. Some couples enjoy it if he puts his penis into her anus. Again, unless the ring of muscle in the anus is very relaxed, this can prove painful so the penis has to be very well lubricated. This way of having sex is called buggery or sodomy and is, in fact, illegal (see page 103).

There are various sex toys available for couples who want to experiment further. These toys are usually very expensive and seldom live up to the wild claims of the manufacturers who are, after all, just in it for the money. Many couples find that a dollop of honey or yoghourt on their sex organs gives them just as much fun for a lot less money.

No two people enjoy sex in exactly the same way, or in the same way each time they have sex. Sometimes he may prefer to make all the movements himself, at other times he may want her to. Likewise, she may at times prefer to take all the initiatives or at other times do what he wants her to do. The best way to find out how your partner likes sex and what turns her or him on is to talk about it together. And talking about sex can be a big turn on in itself.

Petting and bringing each other off in all these ways and many others is a good way of enjoying sex and of giving and getting sexual pleasure without running the risk of getting pregnant. But it's not necessarily a good idea to go just so far but always to draw the line at intercourse. This may lead to a lot of pent-up emotion, and possibly to disappointment when you do have intercourse. It depends what you want, but it would be crazy, for instance, to think of petting as a complete substitute for intercourse on a long-term basis just because you haven't managed to get yourselves fixed up with a reliable method of birth control. (see page 51).

Intercourse

There are so many expressions for sexual intercourse that it's almost impossible to keep track. The technical words are coitus (pronounced coy-tus) and copulation, but they're usually only used by doctors and biology teachers. To make love, to fuck, to lay, to screw, to shag, to have it off or away, to ball, to poke, to shaft, to sleep with, to go to bed with someone and to get your end away are all expressions for the same thing.

The trouble with some of these phrases is that they suggest that intercourse is something that a man does *to* a woman: that the man is the active partner while the woman just lies back and has it all done to her. A man fucks, a woman gets fucked. He screws, she gets screwed. He lays her, she gets laid. Our great grandmothers were told 'Lie on your back and think of Queen and country!' It was probably all the sex education they ever got! So women were brought up to think that *because* they were women they had to be passive and let the man do everything. Men were brought up to think that *because* they were men they had to take all the initiatives and not worry too much about whether the woman was getting any enjoyment from sex — because women weren't really expected to enjoy sex.

'Sex is the price women pay for marriage,' went another silly saying, 'and marriage is the price men pay for sex'. Today there are still many people who believe that women and girls have a lower sex drive than men, which partly explain why words like fuck, screw or lay are seldom used to describe what a female does. But sex doesn't mean one thing for women and something totally different and opposite for men. The important thing for each one of us is to find out for ourselves what we like, regardless of our sex. Fucking, screwing and laying are all things that females and males do *with* each other, not what he does to her.

Under 16?

Sexual intercourse is illegal if the girl is under 16. For details about the law see page 102.

Foreplay

Petting that ends in intercourse is called foreplay. It's a necessary part of having intercourse because it makes our bodies prepared quite naturally for what's going to happen. The penis needs to be erect in order to push it into the vagina. The outer lips of her sex organs need to separate so that the penis can come into contact with the entrance to the vagina. The clitoris can be more easily stimulated when it's poking out of its hood of skin. The walls of the vagina need to produce the fluid that lubricates the sex organs, to make it easier for the penis to slide in and to prevent the clitoris from getting sore when it's rubbed.

The reason it doesn't matter whether a penis is long or short, fat or slim, is that the innermost part of the vagina stretches to whatever length the penis is: it also has very few nerve endings so she can't actually feel the penis right inside her vagina. The walls of the outer third of the vagina, which do have nerve endings, swell and grip the penis whatever its width.

Many girls fear that their vaginas will get too wide if they have too much, sex. Again, because of the way in which the outermost walls swell, it doesn't matter what size a vagina is. It's OK to laugh and joke about cocks so small that they waggle about inside and cunts so slack that cocks get lost – but don't take them seriously. Most penises and vaginas are more or less the same size.

The changes to our bodies during foreplay happen quite naturally while we are getting sexually aroused and as the sexual excitement builds up. Foreplay makes intercourse physically easier – but there's more to it than just that. It gets us into the right mood for intercourse and it gives us a lot of pleasure in itself.

Enjoying Intercourse

When the penis goes into the vagina, it's usually best for it to enter gradually with small thrusts rather than one big plunge – the vagina may take a little time before it expands inside. Either partner can help guide the penis in by holding the lips of her vagina apart and finding the entrance with their finger.

To help give the penis the right stimulation and to give the clitoris as much stimulation as possible you need to move rhythmically from your hips so that the penis slides back and forth inside the vagina.

When the penis slides in and out, the lips of the vagina get pulled too. This can have the effect of pulling the hood of skin back and forth over the head of the clitoris, and so may give it all the rubbing and stimulation it needs. Your movements get faster until one of you comes. If she comes first, she can usually go on moving her hips in thrusting movements until he comes and this may add to her pleasure. But if he comes first, his penis goes limp immediately afterwards and he won't be able to give her clitoris any more stimulation except with his hand or perhaps by rubbing his genitals against hers.

42

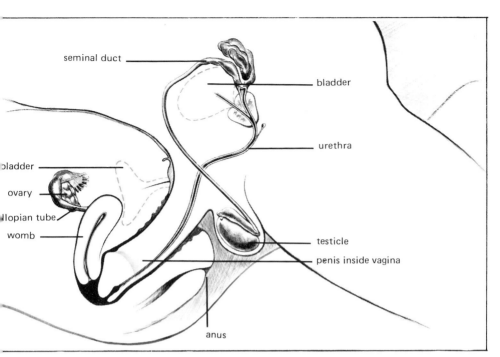

seminal duct

bladder

urethra

bladder

ovary

fallopian tube

womb

testicle

penis inside vagina

anus

This drawing shows a couple having sexual intercourse in the 'missionary' position with the woman on her back and underneath the man — but there are lots of other positions.

Many couples are convinced that the only way to enjoy intercourse 'properly' is to come together, having an orgasm at exactly the same time. In fact this rarely happens. And if it does, it isn't necessarily the great thing some people make it out to be. It's fine if you like it. But if you're so involved in your own orgasm, you might not get the rather special pleasure of seeing your partner come. There's no such thing as a 'proper' way to have sex. Whether you come or not, or precisely when you come, is not nearly as important as how you're feeling and how much you enjoy it.

Positions

There are any number of positions a couple can try. The one most often used in this part of the world is called the missionary position. (When western European missionaries went to 'heathen' lands, it was they who introduced this position. They were amazed to discover that sex could be enjoyed in other positions, and their would-be converts were amazed to discover that this position could be thought all that enjoyable). The couple lie looking at each other with him on top of her, she lies on her back with her legs apart, one on each side of his legs.

Some couples never get around to realising that there's any other way. But it isn't necessarily the best position for her because it means direct stimulation of her clitoris is impossible. Direct stimulation isn't always

43

necessary, but to help her come in this position it may be a good idea to push a pillow or cushion under her bottom and for her to wrap her legs right round his hips.

If the girl sits on top of the man while he lies on his back, she may find it easier to have an orgasm, as either partner can use their fingers to stimulate her clitoris. Both these positions are nice for couples who like to see each other come. The girl can kneel forward on her hands and knees (often called 'doggy-fashion') or can prop herself up on her elbows and the boy can push his penis into her vagina from behind. Or both can lie on their sides in a 'question marks' or 'spoons' position while he enters her from behind. In any position that the boy enters from behind, the girl will probably need to have her clitoris stimulated with a hand.

You can have intercourse standing up (knee-tremblers), sitting down, hanging over the end of the bed, with the girl sitting on a table (table-enders) or chair. Some couples like to try a variety of positions before they come, others prefer to stick on one. Some people like sex in silence, others like to whisper, talk, laugh, cry or shout. Many like sex in a quiet spot in the open air, others like to be in bed. Some like it in the dark, others want the lights on. There are couples who like to be alone and those who enjoy sex with a group of people. But morning or evening, daytime or night time, inside or outside – there's no place, position, time or variation that hasn't been tried or enjoyed (although it's extremely doubtful that anyone *has* ever done it hanging from a chandelier).

Whatever a couple decide to do, whatever variations they hit upon, if both enjoy doing it and find it exciting and satisfying, it's not going to harm anyone. Common sense should tell you if something is dangerous. A good rule of thumb is not to do to anyone else what you wouldn't like them to do to you. Some things may feel new, strange or even peculiar. Don't do them if you don't want to – but you can bet your life it's all been done before. It isn't perverted, abnormal or sick if the aim behind it is to *share* pleasure and if you know you're being careful with someone else's feelings.

It isn't always easy

Enjoying sex and finding out how you and your partner like it isn't always so very easy. Having intercourse for the first time can be a big let down, especially if you don't know what to expect or quite what to do. Like most things, the more often you do it, the better you get. If it does go badly the first time, you won't be the first person to whom this has happened. In fact nearly everyone feels shy and nervous the first time they have intercourse — and also the first time with a particular person.

There are lots of different problems that people come up against at some time or other in their sex lives. This chapter describes some of them: if you think your problem is different, or it isn't mentioned here, don't worry — no two people have exactly identical problems. If you can't sort it out either by yourself or with your partner, there are people specially trained to help. But whatever you do, don't bottle it up. That'll only make things worse.

Virginity

A virgin is someone — female or male — who has never had sexual intercourse. A lot of very harmful rubbish is talked about virginity. Traditionally it's been thought of as something that a girl should keep at all costs and a boy should lose as soon as possible. Girls were expected to treasure their virginity for when 'Mr Right' came along. But if a boy kept his, he was accused of being immature and 'unmanly'. People liked to keep their daughters under-sexed and their sons over-sexed. Again, fear of pregnancy and lack of information on birth control was part of the reason for this, and attitudes are changing. But many of the myths still exist.

For centuries it's been believed that you can tell if a girl is a virgin by her hymen — the thin membrane that covers the entrance to the vagina. If her hymen was unbroken, then she was a virgin; if it was broken then she wasn't. And, of course, the only time a girl was expected or permitted to lose her virginity was on her wedding night. This is the reason why girls were told not

Many girls are born without a hymen, and many hymens, like this one, have holes in them.

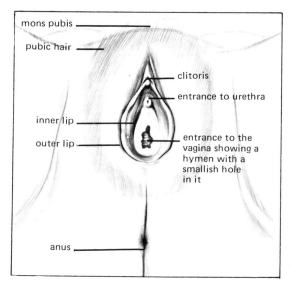

mons pubis

pubic hair

clitoris

entrance to urethra

inner lip

outer lip

entrance to the vagina showing a hymen with a smallish hole in it

anus

to masturbate and why mothers advised their daughters against using tampons — Mr Right might turn out not so right if he discovered his blushing bride had a torn hymen!

For a start, many girls are born without a hymen at all. Many hymens have holes in them so it really isn't possible to tell whether it's broken. And many hymens get stretched or broken quite naturally at a young age by riding a bike or horse or by being constipated, without the girl ever knowing.

A girl can find out for herself what state her hymen is in by pushing a finger up her vagina. If it's still in one piece her finger won't go up more than a few centimetres. If her hymen is in one piece the penis tears a hole in it as it enters her vagina when she has intercourse for the first time. Every time she has intercourse after that her hymen gets rubbed down until there's nothing left but a little ring of tissue that often remains round the entrance to her vagina for the rest of her life.

Most hymens are very thin fragile tissues of skin. Breaking this thin skin can sometimes hurt a little. Some girls can feel when it's being broken, and the tiny blood vessels in it may bleed. Most girls dread this happening, but stories about the amount of pain and blood are usually exaggerations. Some girls feel nothing at all and notice no blood. Others may feel a couple of seconds of pain and there'll be a little bleeding — although seldom enough for her to need to use a sanitary towel or tampon.

The most important thing about virginity is nothing to do with whether you have a hymen or not. Everyone is a virgin at some stage of their life and it's important to be honest about it. Having sex for the first time can be difficult enough, both physically and emotionally, without needing the added complication of a lie about whether or not you're a virgin. Being honest can be awkward if you've been pretending that you've done it all before when you haven't, or that you haven't done it when you have. No close relationship, and certainly not a sexual one, is unaffected by starting off with a lie.

46

The first time — and after

Some girls find that having sex for the first time is so painful that they never want to try again. Most find that the second, third, fourth times and so on are a vast improvement on the first. But just being scared can make it hurt all the more. You need to relax to enjoy sex. Feeling scared or worried that you'll get pregnant or disturbed only makes you feel tense.

Feeling very nervous can sometimes make the muscles in the entrance to the vagina close up very tightly making intercourse impossible. It's only natural for this to happen the first few times. Trying to push on regardless only makes matters worse. If this happens every time and prevents her from ever having intercourse she may need to see a sex therapist to try to sort out the problem.

Some girls find that it hurts every time they have intercourse. This often happens if she has sex just before or during her period when the womb and cervix can be a little tender. Changing to a position in which the vagina gets a chance to stretch out fully — perhaps to the missionary position — will often solve this problem. But the pain could be due to an infection. Even if there is no discharge (the usual sign of an infection) the possibility should be checked out with a doctor (see page 93). If she doesn't want to tell her doctor that she's having sex, she can always say that her tampon is hurting her when she puts it in. .

Ignore the myth that people look different after they've had intercourse for the first time. There's no way of telling whether a girl has had intercourse or not just by looking at her face or by the way she walks. She may feel some soreness in her vagina, but that's all. This is perfectly normal — the vagina won't have had anything as big as a penis in it before. The soreness goes away after a day or two.

If the vagina is dry or doesn't seem to be producing much lubricating fluid of its own, intercourse can be fairly painful for both partners. Most often this is due to trying to have intercourse before she has been stimulated enough — and if she doesn't get enough stimulation she won't be able to have an orgasm. But the vagina doesn't always produce enough of its own lubrication. A spermicidal jelly or cream is a good way of getting the slipperiness you need. A special sterile lubricating jelly called KY Jelly that can be bought from a chemist will also do the trick. Or a lubricated sheath may solve the problem. You'll probably find something around the house like baby oil which will also do. Don't use petroleum jelly if you're using a sheath as it tends to rot the rubber. If all else fails, spit will do.

Many girls get accused of being frigid or cold if they don't want sex, don't seem to enjoy it, if their vaginas don't produce much fluid or if they never have an orgasm. If on the other hand they do want sex or obviously enjoy it a lot, they get called nymphomaniacs. Calling a girl either of these names is very unfair, for if she does have a minor problem to do with sex, it'll just make her worry and suffer all the more. If she's not enjoying sex to the full, the chances are it's simply because she's feeling nervous. Or, perfectly reasonably, it could just mean that she doesn't want sex at that particular time or with that particular person.

Boys who don't seem to want or enjoy sex often think that they're homosexual or are 'undersexed'. The same can be true for a boy as for a girl – he might just not be wanting sex or he may be wanting it at some other time or with some other person. Sex isn't going to be good or very easy for anyone who doesn't feel like it – and no one feels like it all the time or with everyone.

Many boys find that when they have intercourse for the first time they come very quickly indeed, often even before they've had time to get their penis inside the vagina. This is usually nothing more than a simple case of first time nerves and it needn't matter too much. Most find that they can get another erection quite quickly. Some will find however, that this happens every time they have sex – men can get bouts of this problem throughout their lives. Doctors call it premature ejaculation. Some find that the problem is solved by giving themselves a come before they have sex – this makes sure that the sexual excitement builds up more slowly when they're with their partner.

Some suffer from precisely the opposite problem – they can't get an erection or ejaculate however much they want to. This is known by doctors as a form of impotence. Like coming too soon, it's often due to nerves. Those who use a sheath as a means of birth control may find that their penis goes limp as soon as they try to put it on. If this always seems to happen, use another method of birth control (see chapter 8   ). She may be able to help him keep his erection holding the base of his penis quite firmly in her fingers to prevent the blood from flowing out of it. Or she can try squeezing the limp penis into her vagina with her fingers – quite often the penis will grow erect again and they can carry on as if nothing happened.

One of the best ways to solve any sex problem is to talk it over with your sex partner. Sympathy, understanding, discovering together possible reasons for the problem and looking for possible solutions could be all that's needed. But if any problem lasts for a time and doesn't seem to be due to first-time nerves or inexperience, don't just sit there – you can do something. The more you worry and bottle up your fears, the worse the problem will become. Go to your doctor if you think she or he will be sympathetic. Some birth control clinics have doctors specially trained to help people with their sex problems (address, page 115). Give the clinic a ring first to see if they can help, whether you need an appointment and whether there will be a fee. Many of these clinics and centres will be sympathetic to girls and boys under 16.

Sex aids

Sex shops and surgical stores sell a variety of goods that couples can use when they're having sex. Many of these, often very expensive, are supposed to help people who have difficulties when having sex. There are creams and potions which, the manufacturers claim, will make you and your partner rampant and really wild. It's extremely doubtful that they can have any such effect. Most of the creams which are supposed to keep a penis erect for hours or make a girl come have, when analysed little more than oil, water and perfume in them But they don't do any harm and many people are so convinced that they work that they *do* have some effect. There are sheaths with rubber knobs sticking out all over them which are supposed to give a girl feelings of ecstacy. This is doubtful, but, as one doctor has said, if you enjoy looking at a randy sea anemone, it can be money well spent. One warning here – don't use these sheaths as a method of preventing pregnancy without checking – sheaths are only reliable if they carry the British Safety standards kite mark on them

Aphrodisiacs

Aphrodisiacs are substances which supposedly make you feel more sexy. For someone who thinks they have a low sex drive or who has difficulties in getting in the right mood for sex they sound like an answer to a prayer. But in fact there's no such thing as an aphrodisiac. In the past, tomatoes, potatoes, peppers, oysters, musk, powdered rhino horn, sea weed and countless other things have all been thought to have magical powers to make people feel sexy. It is of course true that if we don't eat a good balanced diet we feel less like sex than if we eat fresh healthy foods. But there's no food or drug which can actually make us sexually aroused. A warning about a substance called Spanish Fly. This is a powder made from crushing the bodies of certain beetles which many people believe to be an aphrodisiac. Swallowing Spanish Fly is highly dangerous. It is a poison which can cause – and has caused – death.

Although many sex aids and toys can be fun, they're sold in their tons to people who actually think that they'll cure their sex problems. In fact what they mostly do is to make their manufacturers very rich.

Drugs

People take drugs for a variety of reasons – for fun, to relieve boredom, for curiosity or because they think that drugs can increase the pleasure of sex. The myths that surround drug-taking, are, like all myths, not very reliable.

Drugs don't and can't affect our sex organs. Some, it is true, can lower our inhibitions, relax our muscles and increase our awareness of our bodies to a certain extent. But no two people react in the same way to any one drug. Some drugs can make some people feel good but they can make others feel tensed up, sick and turn them completely off sex.

Unlike sex, drugs are not something that our bodies need naturally. Some drugs are positively dangerous, others are less so. The pleasure we can get from sex depends on how you feel about your sex partner and not on what drugs you take.

Alcohol is a drug which can and does cause just as much physical and mental harm as many drugs which are illegal or available only on prescription.

It is generally believed that alcohol increases the sex drive – 'Three martinis and she's anyone's' being the generally accepted rule of thumb. Drinking a little can lower our inhibitions to make us feel less shy, but basically, alcohol is a depressant. The main problem with alcohol is that it only requires a small amount to stop people from thinking too clearly. This makes it easy to go on drinking and become really drunk and ill. Too much alcohol will make you feel sleepy, put you off sex and make it difficult to have an orgasm. It has the unhappy effect of making us feel randy but decreasing the quality (or likelihood) of performance. Many boys find that once they're drunk they can't get an erection – 'brewers, or drinkers, droop' as it's often called.

Despite the havoc and unhappiness that alcohol can cause, it's a socially acceptable drug. But like all drugs, whether legal or illegal, it's the manufacturers and sellers who profit in the end.

Birth control

When a boy ejaculates there are millions of tiny sperms in his semen. It only takes one of these sperms to make a girl pregnant. What happens is this: the sperms swim up the vagina, into the womb and up the Fallopian tubes. If any one sperm meets a ripe egg on its way down from an ovary towards the womb it may pierce the wall of the egg and enter it. The egg is then fertilised by the sperm – the process is known as conception. Once this has happened the girl is said to have conceived and she is pregnant. The fertilised egg travels down the Fallopian tube and, once in the womb, it settles on the thickened walls of the womb.

Every single time a girl and boy have intercourse a baby may be conceived. The only way of making sure that a girl doesn't get pregnant is, quite simply, not to have intercourse. But if you want to have sex and not have a baby, you must use a really reliable method of birth control or contraception. In technical terms, contraception means 'against conception'. In human terms it means that a girl does not get pregnant.

Facts and figures can seem rather unreal, but think of the possible human misery behind these:

— every year, one in three girls under twenty getting married is pregnant. (Did they want to be pregnant? Did they or their boyfriends really want to get married?)
— every year, more than 23,000 unmarried teenage girls become mums. (How did they feel about that? How did their families and boyfriends feel? How do the kids who get born feel?)
— every year, more than 28,000 teenage girls have operations called abortions to end their pregnancies. (How does this affect the girls, their families and boyfriends? How much did it cost them? Could they really afford it? How many others had abortions that don't show up on the statistics?)
— every year, thousands and thousands of girls are scared out of their minds because they think that they might be pregnant.

*Ignore the myths about birth control
get good advice from an expert*

It all adds up to an awful lot of misery for a lot of people. And it could nearly all be prevented. The answer is: contraception.

Until about ten years ago, it wasn't easy to get advice about contraceptives unless you were married. But today it's a relatively simple matter to find out how you can have sex with virtually no risk of getting pregnant if that's what you want. The methods are free or quite cheap, and easy to use. Though it's more difficult to get contraceptive advice in some parts of the country than others, more and more doctors now realise how important it is that every baby should be a wanted baby, and that the way to prevent unwanted babies from being born is to give people advice about birth control methods. The birth control clinics listed on page 115 are helpful and friendly – they won't worry about your age or whether you're married or unmarried. The doctors and clinics are there to help – don't take risks.

Every method of birth control involves some thinking and planning in advance. Some people think that preparing for sex is cold-blooded and

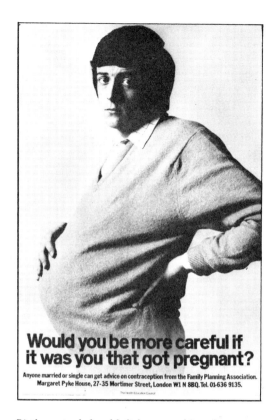

Would you be more careful if it was you that got pregnant?

Anyone married or single can get advice on contraception from the Family Planning Association. Margaret Pyke House, 27-35 Mortimer Street, London W1 N 8BQ. Tel. 01-636 9135.

The Health Education Council

Birth control shouldn't be something that only girls have to think about just because they're the ones to get pregnant

unromantic. If you think that taking the risk of getting pregnant is 'romantic' you should think again, carefully. How much 'romance' is there going to be around if you, or your girlfriend, get pregnant?

Sex can, and often does 'just happen', but it's not worth chancing it. Unless you think in advance and take precautions, once a sperm gets into the vagina there's nothing you can do but cross your fingers and hope. And hoping never stopped anyone from getting pregnant. It is true that no contraceptive is absolutely foolproof or one hundred per cent safe – but the least safe method is using no contraceptive at all.

The Myths

The myths about preventing a pregnancy probably do more harm than any of the other myths about sex. Do NOT believe anyone who claims (or worse, tries to persuade you) that any of the following 'methods' will prevent you from getting pregnant:

53

- if you have sex standing up
- if she jumps up and down, coughs or sneezes after sex
- if she doesn't have an orgasm
- if she has a hot bath immediately before sex
- if she has a hot bath immediately after sex
- if she pees immediately after sex
- if she washes out her vagina with lemon juice, vinegar, coca-cola (or anything else) immediately after sex
- if you have sex during, just before or just after her period.

These methods DON'T work, CAN'T work and NEVER worked.

A girl isn't necessarily going to get pregnant every time she has sex without using a contraceptive. This is probably why so many people think that there are definite times of the month when it is 'safe' to have sex without needing to use a contraceptive. But this isn't true – the risk is there every time. Girls have got pregnant by having sex during, before and after their period. And for many girls, getting pregnant happens very easily indeed.

Whose Responsibility?

It takes two to make a baby. It should take two to work out the best way not to make one. Birth control is something every couple should talk over together before they have sex.

Many girls get so used to letting their boyfriends take all the decisions that they grow to think that it's his job to worry about contraception. Many boys reckon that because it's the girl who gets pregnant, it's her job to make sure she doesn't. But not all methods suit everybody and unless you talk it over together you may not find out which is the best method for you. The responsibility has got to be shared as well as the fun and the pleasure. After all, any baby that's conceived will be a part of you both.

The two most reliable methods of birth control are the Pill and the coil (or IUD). Unfortunately, they're also the ones for which women have to take the main responsibility and which have the most unpleasant side effects. One of the next most reliable methods, the sheath, is mostly the boy's responsibility and it's probably the method most disliked by boys, because it tends to numb feeling and for some it's embarrassing to put it on. But the responsibility for all methods can be shared in one way or another whether it's helping to put on the sheath or reminding a girl to take her Pill.

Legal Position

It is against the law for a boy to have intercourse with a girl who is under 16 but it isn't illegal to use or get contraceptives if she's under age (see page 102). Of the four most reliable methods – the Pill, the coil, the cap-plus-spermicide and the sheath – only the sheath is available without medical advice. Some doctors will want to tell a girl's parents if she asks for the Pill or the coil or the cap. If she can discuss it all with her parents, well and good. But if she doesn't want them to know, she must tell her doctor this very firmly. Many doctors will then agree to go ahead and prescribe the contraceptives. Others won't, and may suggest another method. (The only other reliable method left is the sheath). A girl can then either decide that her boyfriend should use the sheath as a way of preventing pregnancy or she can go to another doctor or clinic.

Since your National Health Service (NHS) medical card has your date of birth printed on it, there's no point in pretending that you're over sixteen if you're not. None of the clinics mentioned on page 115 will check up on your age, but if a girl wants the Pill or coil they may ask her permission to tell her parents or family doctor. If she refuses this permission, they may go ahead and help anyway. Many doctors now recognise that any girl or boy who thinks seriously about not getting pregnant is acting responsibly.

Where to get Contraception

Family doctors: can provide the following free: the Pill, the coil, the cap and spermicide. Some doctors prefer to send their patients to a local family planning clinic. Because some methods can have painful or dangerous side effects if used by girls who have had certain illnesses, a doctor who knows all about their medical history can be the best person to get advice and supplies from.

Clinics: also provide advice and supplies, usually free, to both girls and boys. Doctors or trained workers at the clinics are very helpful and friendly and can often spend more time than a family doctor with each patient, which gives them an advantage. For addresses of these centres and clinics, see page 115 or look up in the phone book or Yellow Pages under Family Planning.

Chemists: prescriptions for the Pill can be taken to the pharmacy counter of a chemist shop. Not all chemists carry very large stocks of all brands. Sheaths, spermicides and the cap can be bought over the counter (but the cap must be fitted first by a doctor or nurse to make sure you get the right size and shape).

Surgical stores etc: sell the cap, spermicides and sheaths. Some hairdressing shops (usually male) sell sheaths. Slot machines for sheaths can be found in some changing rooms, public toilets and pubs. Warning: sheaths perish with age and slot machines may have out-of-date and unreliable brands.

Live in Eire?

The only method of birth control approved by the Roman Catholic Church is the unreliable rhythm method (see page 65). As a result, it's illegal in Eire to sell or buy contraceptives. But it isn't illegal to *use* them. If you're married, you can bring supplies into the country for your own use. It's possible to find a doctor who will prescribe the Pill supposedly 'to regulate periods' (which it does do), so quite a few Irish women are now on the Pill. The organisations on page 115 will help anyone married or unmarried and whatever their age with advice and supplies.

Apart from sheaths, all birth control methods are available free from doctors and clinics except in Eire. Some clinics, although not profit-making, have to charge a fee for the advice and help they give. Sheaths cost about 10p each and usually come in packs of three or more.

The Pill

Reliability

If the instructions are followed exactly, the Pill is one hundred per cent effective.

The Pill contains two chemicals, or artificial hormones (oestrogen and progesterone), which prevent an egg from ripening in an ovary and from being released from the ovary. If no egg is released, there's absolutely no chance of a girl getting pregnant. The only reason why the Pill is not totally one hundred per cent safe is that many women forget to take them regularly and don't follow the instructions on the packet properly.

Different brands

There are over thirty different brands, all a bit different and containing different amounts of the chemical hormones. Most packs have 21 Pills in them: you take one each day for three weeks, stop for seven days when you have your period, and then start a new pack. Other brands have Pills that you take every day of the year. All packs have instructions with them, but always ask your doctor or clinic to explain them as well. (Some manufacturers are better at making Pills than writing instructions). If a certain brand gives a girl any unwelcome effects (see below) she'll have to go back to her doctor or clinic until she finds one that suits her. Some girls never find a make of Pill to suit them and have to use another method of birth control.

Points to remember

Swallow a Pill at the same time every day — perhaps on waking up or just before going to sleep — as this makes it easier to remember them. Follow the instructions on the pack *exactly*. For the first two weeks of taking the Pill, or of taking a new brand, another method of birth control *must* be used as well. They must be swallowed every day and not just after having sex. Never lend, borrow or mix brands — because they don't work if you do. If a girl forgets to take her Pill one day, she must take two the next day as soon as she remembers. If she forgets for two days on the trot, she must take all three Pills as soon as she remembers, but she must then also use another birth control method until her next period starts. Being sick or having diarrhoea can get rid of the Pill from the body before it's been absorbed, so another Pill should be taken as soon as possible and another method of birth control must be used until the next period.

Annoying side effects

While her body is getting used to the new hormone level of the Pill, a girl may feel all or some of the following side effects: tiredness, sickness (often in the morning), bleeding in between her periods, headaches, irritability, sore breasts, vaginal infections; and she may put on several pounds in weight. Sometimes a period is missed as a result of being on the Pill. Any girl who misses a period and thinks she could be pregnant, should have a pregnancy test. (see page 70)

Many of these side effects go away after a month or two. If they last any longer, she must go back to her doctor or clinic and ask for another brand. If the doctor isn't very sympathetic and thinks she just has to put up with these complaints, the best plan is to go to another doctor or clinic.

Serious side effects

Not everyone is convinced that enough research has been done on the Pill for us to know about all the possible side effects. Recent evidence suggests that the Pill should not be taken for more than about 15 years and not at all by older women (30-35). It's possible that some people exaggerate the dangers because they don't like the thought of women being able to control quite so easily and efficiently the number of babies they have — there are still a surprising number of people around who think you should only have sex if you plan to have babies! However, there is some evidence that bloodclotting (thrombosis) and heart disease is linked to taking the Pill, which is why girls who have a medical history of blood clots or heart disease should not take the Pill. It's extremely unlikely that there's any connection between the Pill and cancer.

Some women find that taking the Pill makes them lose all sexual desire. If this happens then the Pill is not the method for them.

Girls who are diabetic, epileptic, asthmatic, who get migraine headaches, who suffer from high or low blood pressure, who have had a liver disease or a blood clot must tell their doctor and, if they take the Pill at all, should only do so under close medical supervision.

Any side effect that lasts for more than 2-3 months *must* be reported to the doctor or clinic.

Disadvantages

Most of the possible disadvantages have been described under the above section on side effects. For a girl who doesn't want her parents to know she's on the Pill, hiding the packet may prove a problem. It's *not* a good idea to take them out of their packet and put them in a bottle as this makes it almost impossible to remember whether they've been taken each day. Many women dislike taking artificial hormones and chemicals because so little is known about the possible consequences.

Advantages

As long as the instructions are followed exactly the Pill gives complete protection against unwanted pregnancies. Many women find that once they're

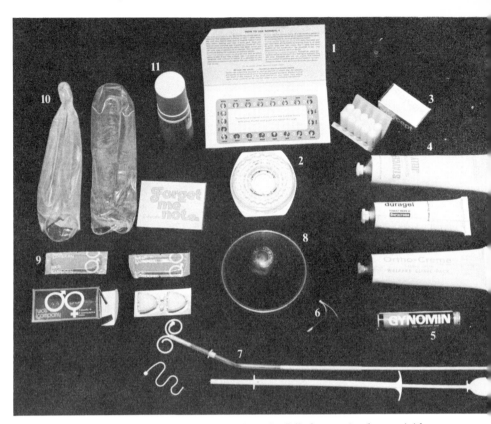

Different methods of birth control 1. & 2. the Pill; 3. a pack of spermicide pessaries; 4. three different brands of spermicide jelly and cream; 5. a tube of spermicide pessaries; 6. the 'Copper 7' coil; 7. two types of coils with their inserters; 8. a diaphragm or cap; 9. a brand of sheath that comes with a spermicide to be placed in the vagina; 10. two unrolled sheaths, one with a teat, the other without; 11. an aerosol can of spermicide foam.

on the Pill all their worries and fears about getting pregnant disappear and their sex life improves enormously. The Pill often makes women feel much better just before their periods and it usually makes periods much shorter and less painful. It may clear up a spotty complexion.

The Mini Pill

Reliability
Out of every hundred women who take the mini-pill for a year, about two get pregnant.

How it works
Many doctors believe that some of the side effects of the ordinary Pill are caused by oestrogen, one of the two artifical hormones. The mini-pill has only one of these hormones (progesterone) and was introduced to solve these

58

problems. This particular hormone makes the mucus inside the neck of the womb much thicker than usual and so sperms find it impossible to get through and into the womb and Fallopian tubes.

Points to remember
The mini-pill has to be swallowed every single day of the year. It *must* be taken absolutely regularly and at exactly the same time each day. If it's taken even a few hours later than usual on one day, it may not prevent pregnancy.

Disadvantages
It's not as reliable as the ordinary Pill and even less is known about the possible long-term side effects. It often causes heavy and irregular periods for the first few months. Many women find it almost impossible to take at the same time every day because they don't lead clockwork lives.

Advantages
It's a good Pill for girls who are overweight or who have a personal or family medical history of bloodclotting, diabetes, asthma, epilepsy, migraine or liver disease.

Coil (Intrauterine device, IUD, loop)

Reliability
Out of every hundred women who use the coil for a year, about two get pregnant.

How it works
Intrauterine means 'inside the uterus', which is where the coil is fitted. They're small, flat, flexible devices, (or plastic and copper) which only a properly trained person can fit into the womb. They come in various shapes. The types most often used in Britain are the Lippes loop, the Safe-T-Coil and the Copper 7. They all have a couple of threads attached to the end.

No one is quite sure how the coil works. It touches the womb in several places and seems to prevent a fertilised egg from attaching itself to the sides of the womb. It's also thought that it makes the egg travel down the Fallopian tube much faster than usual so that the lining of the womb just isn't ready to accept a fertilised egg when it has arrived there. It is possible that the coil irritates the womb lining and large white blood cells are then produced in the womb which destroy the egg and sperms.

Inserting the coil
Fitting a coil into the womb is quite simple but it has to be done by someone who is specially trained. Not all family doctors are trained to do it so it may be better and safer to go to one of the clinics mentioned on page 115. Anyone can be fitted with a coil although it used to be thought that only women who had had a baby could have them. (Some doctors and clinics still won't give the coil to a girl who hasn't had a baby). The Copper 7 is the type most often given to girls and women who haven't had a baby.

Every coil, whatever its shape, is flexible enough to be pressed into a straight line and put into a very narrow tube. This tube is then gently pushed into the vagina, and up into the womb through the very narrow opening in the cervix. The coil is pushed out of this tube by a plunger and it goes back to its original shape. The inserter tube is then pulled out, leaving the coil in the womb with its threads hanging down through the cervix into the very top of the vagina.

The whole process is very quick — less than half a minute or so. It can hurt, sometimes quite a lot, especially if the girl is very tense. But some women hardly feel a thing.

Disadvantages

The womb isn't used to having anything solid in it and so it often tries to push the coil out. This can cause cramp pains and bleeding — especially just after it's been inserted. Pills normally taken for period pains and a hot water bottle can make a girl feel more comfortable.

You have to go to the doctor or clinic to have the coil removed but sometimes the coil gets pushed out of its own accord. Some girls find it stays in the second or third time, others find that they can never keep one in. Because it's so easy for an IUD to be pushed out and flushed away unnoticed, a girl must check that it's still there once a week. The best way to do this is in the bath or squatting down, pushing a finger or two up inside the vagina and feeling for the little threads. If the threads aren't there or the coil itself can be felt pushing its way out, a visit to the doctor or clinic is called for. In the meantime another birth control method must be used.

A coil can cause more serious complications. It's been noticed that many women with coils develop severe infections in their internal sex organs. Very rarely, it can pierce the wall of the womb. Any severe pain or bleeding should be reported to the doctor immediately. So should continued pain of any kind.

A girl with a coil who misses a period or become pregnant should also immediately visit her doctor. It can cause complications during pregnancy, although not always, but a doctor will have to make sure.

Advantages

The coil can be put in and forgotten — apart from the girl's own weekly check. The Copper 7s have to be changed every two years. It's one of the few birth control methods that's completely separate from sex — once it's in you don't have to think about birth control again. It's almost as safe as the Pill but doesn't involve taking chemicals or produce any of their side effects.

Sheath (Condom, johnny, french letter, noddy, rubber, 'durex', safe, preventitive, prophylactic etc)

Reliability

Out of every hundred couples using the sheath for a year, about four women become pregnant. It's even more reliable when used with a spermicide as well (see page 64).

How it works

A sheath is made of very thin rubber and fits on to an erect penis before intercourse. When the boy ejaculates, his semen and sperms stay inside the sheath. This means that the sperms don't get into the vagina and can't swim up into the womb.

It has to be put on very carefully, holding the closed end firmly between the fingers and thumb while it's being rolled down over the erect penis. This keeps the air out of the tip, leaving a space for the semen to go into. The sheath could burst at the crucial moment if there's any air in it.

After the boy's had his orgasm, the rim of the sheath at the base of his penis must be held very firmly while he pulls it out of the girl's vagina. If any sperms get spilled into the vagina at this stage you might as well not have bothered to use a sheath at all. It's a good idea for a girl to use some sperm-killing chemical in her vagina, in case this happens.

Points to remember

It's important that the sheath is rolled on to the penis before the penis touches any part of a girl's sex organs. The small quantity of semen which sometimes leaks out of his penis before a boy comes can contain sperms and may make her pregnant, even if the penis hasn't been inside her.

There are many different brands of sheath to choose from. The lubricated ones can make intercourse easier. Those with a small bag, or teat, at the end provide a space for the semen and are less likely to burst. The coloured ones may be more fun.

ALWAYS use a brand that carries the British Safety Standards kite-mark.

Disadvantages

Many boys complain that wearing a sheath is a bit like trying to play the guitar with gloves on! They do tend to cut down a bit on sensation. Because he has to withdraw immediately after he's come, many girls who either haven't come themselves or who like to feel a penis inside them can feel a bit disappointed. Having to interrupt everything while you reach for and unwrap a sheath can cause some problems — especially if he finds his penis shrinks at this stage.

Advantages

They're easy to buy and simple to use. Many couples find the whole business of putting them on — and it's something you can do together — a real turn on. They help to prevent the spread of sexually transmitted diseases. Doctors who are worried by the number of young girls who get tendencies towards cancer of the cervix recommend the sheath (see also page 100).

Warning: there are mini-sheaths that cover only the tip of the penis called 'grecian tips' or 'american tips'. These are totally useless – DON'T use them.

Diaphragm plus spermicide (cap, Dutch cap)

Reliability
Out of every hundred women using the diaphragm with sperm-killing chemical for a year, about four get pregnant.

How it works
A diaphragm looks a bit like a small shallow bowl. The dome is made of thin rubber and the thicker rim is made of flexible wire covered in rubber. There are some smaller plastic types (called cervical caps) for girls who are allergic to rubber.

They fit inside the vagina and close off the entrance to the womb so that sperms all stay in the vagina. If any do manage to wriggle past they're killed by the spermicide, which must be used with a cap.

Fitting
No two girls have exactly the same size or shape vagina so everyone has to be fitted individually by her doctor or clinic. She'll be given an internal examination which involves lying on her back with her legs spread apart. The doctor or nurse will gently feel inside her vagina with their fingers and show her how to put the cap in. Don't leave the clinic or doctor until you've tried putting it in yourself and can do it easily. After a bit of practice they're very easy to use.

How to use
A cap has to be put in place no more than three hours before intercourse. A splurge of spermicide cream or jelly (about a teaspoonful) must be smeared on each side of the dome, and some more spread all the way round the rim. The cap is then squeezed between the fingers and thumb into a cigar shape and pushed up into the vagina so that the cervix is completely covered. A girl must then check if it's properly in place with her finger. The cap must cover the cervix. This feels like a small knob right up inside the vagina. When the cap's in place, this knob can be felt behind the centre of the cap.

If you have intercourse more than three hours after putting the cap in, don't remove it but squeeze some more spermicide up your vagina. (Spermicides come with special applicators just for this purpose). Don't take it out for at least six hours, preferably eight hours, after intercourse to make sure that all the sperms are killed, and don't leave it in for more than twenty four hours. It's usually easier to take it out by crouching or lifting one leg up.

Points to remember
Never borrow or lend your cap – your friend isn't necessarily going to be the same size or shape. Go for another fitting if you put on or lose more than half

62

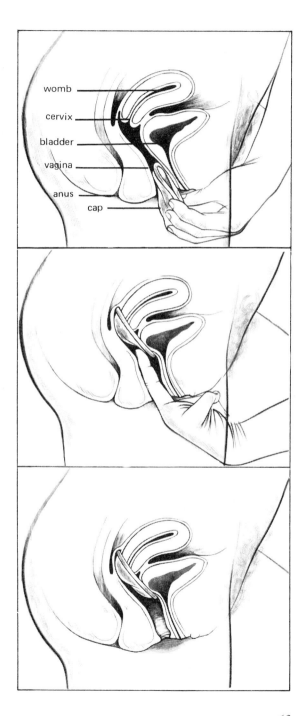

Putting in a cap
1 Putting the cap into position

2 Always check that the cap is properly in position by feeling with your finger

3 In this diagram the cap is in position – the cervix is safely covered by the cap

63

a stone in weight. If you get fitted for a cap before you've ever had intercourse you must go for another fitting afterwards – you may need another size.

After use, the cap must be washed gently in warm water and mild soap, rinsed and then dried *very* thoroughly. Inspect for defects or tears by holding it up to the light. If it gets bent out of shape, just bend the rim gently back to its circular shape.

A cap can't disappear up inside or get stuck in the vagina. The only way out for anything as big as a cap is the way it went in.

Disadvantages

Having to think about putting in a cap before sex can be a bit of a drawback. It is possible for a cap to slip or get pushed out of place during intercourse which is why they should ALWAYS be used with a spermicide. Sometimes the cap can be felt by the tip of the penis – although this shouldn't happen if it's properly in place. It occasionally feels a bit uncomfortable to take the cap out.

Advantages

If used properly, looked after carefully (beware of long finger nails) and always used with a spermicide, caps are a reliable method of birth control. Many women like to feel that they're not swallowing chemicals or placing some metal or plastic object permanently into their wombs and yet are still controlling for themselves whether or not they get pregnant. Caps are also a good way of temporarily holding back the flow if you have sex during a period. Like the sheath, some doctors believe that the cap may help prevent a tendency towards cancer of the cervix (see page 100).

Spermicides

Reliability

NOT reliable on their own. MUST be used with the sheath or cap.

How it works

There are three main types of chemical contraceptives that kill sperms: jellies and creams, tablets (called pessaries) and aerosol foams. The foams both kill sperms and make a thick barrier so that sperms can't swim into the womb. The jellies and creams come with a plunger-type applicator that you push into your vagina.

Disadvantages

Use only the brands recommended by the doctor or clinic – some brands can make caps and sheaths perish and can cause soreness if either girl or boy is allergic to the chemical. After sex the spermicides leak out which can be rather messy, but the girl shouldn't have a bath until about six hours after because water and soap can get inside and dilute or affect the spermicide. Couples who enjoy each other's natural tastes and smells find that spermicides don't taste too good.

No prescription is needed – you can buy them at any chemist – although they're very expensive and you can get them free from the clinic. Some brands help prevent the spread of sexually transmitted diseases.

Warning: Ignore all claims made by manufacturers that spermicides can be used on their own – they can't. One particular brand, called 'C-Film' (advertised as the first his-and-hers contraceptive) which supposedly fits over the tip of the penis or can be put inside the vagina, should NOT be used as a contraceptive.

Sterilisation

All the birth control methods described above can be reversed. That's to say anyone who decides they do want a baby can simply stop using whatever method it is that they've been using. Sterilisation is not reversible. Although some women and men who have been sterilised and then changed their minds have had operations to reverse the original one, there's no guarantee that this can be done.

For women, sterilisation involves an operation either to tie off both Fallopian tubes or burn the ends of the tubes so that no egg ever reaches the womb.

For men, an operation called a vasectomy is done, tying off the tubes in his testicles which carry the sperm to the semen. He can still have a perfectly normal orgasm and ejaculation, but there aren't any sperms in the semen.

Anyone wanting to be sterilised must be absolutely sure that they won't want children in the future. Doctors dislike doing these operations on anyone who is under 30, unmarried or hasn't had at least one child.

The operation used to be done only if it was thought that the mother might have diseased babies. There have been cases of parents or guardians arranging for young girls to be sterilised for this reason. This is very rare and after a big legal case in 1975, is unlikely to ever happen again.

Methods not to be used unless you don't mind if you have a baby.

Rhythm method

Out of every hundred couples who use this method for a year, up to thirty will get pregnant.

Many girls and boys have a vague idea that there are certain times of the month when it is 'safe' to have sex, and they won't get pregnant. Depending on what they've heard, some think it's safe to have sex during a girl's period, and others think it's safe either just before or just after her period. The truth is that no one can EVER be sure of when it is or isn't safe, so in fact it is NEVER safe.

Rhythm is the only method of birth control approved by the Roman Catholic Church. Because of this and because it's always a bit of a gamble, it's sometimes known as 'Vatican Roulette'. The Roman Catholic Church only approves of sex for married couples and there are no advantages for an unmarried couple who do not want a baby using this method.

It's also known as the 'safe period' method. Ignore this. Nothing could be less safe than trying to avoid getting pregnant by using this method. Married Roman Catholic couples who want to use the rhythm method have to be given highly detailed and accurate advice by their doctor or clinic on how to try to use this complicated method of birth control. It takes a year to work out, and is different for every single woman.

There is NO day when a girl can be absolutely sure that she will definitely not get pregnant.

Withdrawal (coitus interruptus, pulling out in time, being careful)

Reliability

Out of every hundred couples using this method for a year, about seventeen get pregnant.

How it works

Just before he has his orgasm, the boy has to pull his penis out of the vagina and make sure that no sperms get anywhere near her vagina.

Disadvantages

This 'method' accounts for a high number of unwanted babies and teenage pregnancies. Sperms can leak from the penis before a boy ejaculates – and it only takes one particularly hardy sperm to make a girl pregnant. It can be very difficult for a boy to withdraw in time, however experienced he is.

It can also limit the possible positions in which you can have sex – it is very difficult for a couple to suddenly spring apart at just the right time if she is sitting on top of him. Withdrawing suddenly can spoil his orgasm and can also spoil sex for her. It's very doubtful that she will ever be able to feel really satisfied if this 'method' is used.

Holding back (coitus reservatus)

Reliability

NOT reliable.

According to the rule of this 'method', once the penis has entered the vagina, you both have to lie absolutely still and wait for the penis to go limp and little. And that's it! The boy then pulls out his penis without either of you having an orgasm.

As with withdrawing, it's very possible for some sperms to leak out of the penis before the boy has an orgasm. The amount of self control needed is enormous. It's difficult to imagine how anyone could possibly enjoy sex by this method.

Douche (pronounced 'doosh')

NOT reliable — possibly *increases* the chances of pregnancy.

A douche (which is the French word for a shower) is a rubber bulb which is filled with a special chemical. It has a long rubber tube attached which is pushed into the vagina. By squeezing the bulb, the solution rushes into the vagina and washes it out. Immediately after she's had intercourse a girl is supposed to run into the bathroom and use her douche. The big problem with this as a birth control method is that sperms swim into the womb a whole lot quicker than anyone can run to the bathroom. And instead of killing sperms and washing them out, the pressure of the solution may actually help push sperms *into* the womb.

Warning: Some doctors recommend a douche to cure certain vaginal infections — other doctors believe that it's possible to damage a girl's internal sex organs in this way. Should only ever be used under close medical supervision.

The future

It must be obvious by now that we don't yet have anything like the perfect method of birth control — getting pregnant is often nothing more than an accident. Research is constantly being done to find new methods and to improve old ones. The following methods aren't generally available but if you want to find out more about them contact the Family Planning Association (see page 115).

These pills are still very much in the experimental stage. They contain a hormone which destroys the fertilised egg before it reaches the womb.

They're taken either a few hours before intercourse or a few hours after. Can't be taken more than five times a week.

All-year-round protection

Doctors are experimenting with a drug which is injected into a woman's body and prevents conception for several months. It's being used in many under-developed countries but it's illegal in Britain and the USA. So far the side effects are much more serious than those from the Pill – it's thought that it makes women infertile, so they can never have any babies.

Menstrual extraction

This method of birth control is done a day or two (but no more) after intercourse, when there's no way of being sure whether or not a girl is pregnant. A thin flexible tube is pushed into the vagina, through the opening in the cervix and into the womb. A suction device is fitted to the other end and it draws out the contents of the womb. It takes only a moment or two and is usually pretty painless.

It's used quite widely in America – often by women who simply don't want the bother of having their periods. It isn't used much in Britain yet, although some clinics do it. It could be a very good method of birth control for women who only have sex now and again. As an emergency measure, when a contraceptive has failed – perhaps a sheath burst or a Pill was forgotten – it can be extremely useful.

Pill for men?

Since so much more is known about the internal sex organs of men than of women, it may seem surprising that there's no contraceptive pill for men. The two most reliable contraceptives – the Pill and the coil – can both have unpleasant side effects for women. Many people have a strong suspicion that the (mainly male) scientists who have worked in this area don't like the thought of mucking about with their own sex organs. There are some scientists doing research into finding a reliable birth control drug for men but so far tests have proved successful on male rats but not on humans.

Pregnancy

How to tell

It's not always easy for a girl to tell if she's pregnant. As soon as the egg has been fertilised by a sperm, hormones are produced which prevent any more eggs from ripening and she won't have any more periods until the pregnancy is ended. So missing a period may be the first sign of pregnancy. But few girls ever know exactly when to expect their periods – they're often very irregular. A late period or missing out on one altogether can also be because a girl's hormones haven't yet become properly balanced or simply the result of dieting, over-tiredness, a change in routine or an emotional upset. Worrying about being pregnant can also make her miss a period. Whether or not she's having sex often or at all, it's a good idea for a girl to keep a record of when she has her periods so she'll have some idea of whether her period is late or how late it is. There can be several other signs of pregnancy. Morning sickness – either feeling or being sick – is common during the first three months of a pregnancy. Her breasts may swell slightly and feel a bit sore.

If she hasn't had sex since her last period then she's probably not pregnant but occasionally there are false periods in early pregnancy. Some light bleeding lasting maybe only a day or two, plus some other signs like tiredness, sickness and wanting to pee frequently probably mean that a girl is pregnant. Once her period is two weeks late, and she thinks she could be pregnant, the only way to find out for certain is to have a pregnancy test done.

No test can be accurate until a period is fourteen days overdue. Even then it may not be accurate. If the result is positive (meaning that she's pregnant) then she almost certainly is. But a negative result, which should mean she's not pregnant, may be wrong. A girl who gets a negative result should have another test done every four or five days until her next period is due to make absolutely sure and to find out as early as possible. If she misses two periods in a row she must go to her doctor or clinic.

Once she's missed two periods, a doctor will be able to tell if she's pregnant by giving her an internal examination. This involves lying on your back with your legs spread apart. The doctor will wear a lubricated glove to feel inside your vagina. This won't hurt but it may be uncomfortable.

Many girls waste valuable time just hoping that their period will come. But the sooner you find out the sooner you'll be able to get the necessary advice. Speed is essential if you think you may want an abortion.

Despite all the rumours, there are no pills or medicines that a doctor can prescribe or that you can buy which will bring on your period if you are pregnant. There are pills that doctors can prescribe which bring on a period in a girl who isn't pregnant, but few doctors like prescribing these for a young girl.

Some girls think they can bring on their period by taking a hot bath or jumping down flights of stairs or taking a bike ride over a bumpy field. They're probably more than half hoping that if they *are* pregnant this will give them a miscarriage. But none of these or any other methods work. If they did, all women would be able to have their periods whenever they wanted, or they'd have them every time they fell over!

Pregnancy testing

To get a pregnancy test done you have to collect a sample of the first pee of the day. You need a small clean bottle or jar with an airtight lid. An old pill bottle or small herb jar is ideal. Wash it out first with some nearly boiling water.

The testers will find it useful to know the exact date when your last period started, your age and the name of any drugs you're taking – including birth control pills. If you don't know what the drugs are called take the bottle with you or explain what they're for.

Where to go

Family doctor

Your own doctor is probably the best person to go to, although it takes a day or two to get the results. If you're under sixteen, your doctor may want to tell your parents. If you don't want them to know, tell your doctor firmly. You'll have to go back in a day or two for the result. If it's negative you may get a lecture or you may get good birth control advice. If it's positive, your doctor will be able to give you the medical advice you need, but she or he may be opposed to abortion.

Health Authority Clinics

Phone your local hospital or town hall to get the address of your Area Health Authority Clinic which will do the test free of charge.

Charitable Pregnancy Advisory Services

Several charitable pregnancy advisory clinics and centres provide reliable pregnancy testing services (addresses, page 115), free at some, costing up to £2 at others. Yellow Pages list all these clinics under 'Pregnancy Test

Services'. Phone first to check opening hours and cost. Some will give you the result while you wait. If you are pregnant, you will get good advice and help on what do to at these organisations.

Postal Services
There are many private commercial laboratories which charge up to £5. They advertise widely in newspapers, magazines, on public transport and on hoardings. They are also listed in the Yellow Pages under Pregnancy Test Services. Phone first to find out the cost. Use a plastic bottle and attach all details firmly to the bottle. Pack carefully and enclose the fee. The laboratory will either send the result or can be phoned up a few days later.

Women's Centres
In several large cities there are women's centres which run their own testing services. If they don't, they'll tell you where you can go. They won't charge but may suggest a small donation towards the cost. They'll give good, friendly but not necessarily expert advice. To find your local centre see page 120.

Chemist shops
Many chemist shops provide a testing service for a fee of up to £4. There'll be a small notice in the pharmacy section advertising the service. The result may be ready the same day or the next. You have to take the sample in, but ask if you can phone for the result.

Do-It-Yourself Kits
For about £3 it's possible to buy a kit and do your own test. The kit includes a test tube, some chemicals and instructions. Not recommended, as it's very easy to do it wrongly.

If you're not pregnant

The only way to make sure you don't have to go through all that worry and hassle again is to make sure that you use a really reliable method of birth control. (See page 51).

If you were using an effective contraceptive, go back and read the chapter again to check whether you've been using it properly.

If you are pregnant

A girl who is pregnant but didn't plan to be very soon has to make a decision. She has three choices: keeping the baby, arranging for it to be adopted or fostered, or getting an abortion. If you're under 16 you can't get married (see page 83). Some girls plan to keep their baby and marry the father as soon as they're old enough. For anyone under sixteen the chances are that the decision will be taken for them. But it may not be the right decision. Try to work out in your own mind what you want and why. If your parents try to persuade you to have your baby and get it adopted, but you want an abortion, it won't be easy to do what you want to do. But it may be possible.

First reactions
Doubtless if you didn't intend getting pregnant your first reaction will be one of panic. This doesn't help, but it's natural to think that your whole life, career and family will be in ruins. In fact, nothing need be ruined, although this won't be easy to imagine at the time.

Some girls who can't face the family reaction decide just to run away from home. This is a very bad idea. With nowhere to go or stay, worse things than being pregnant can happen to you, especially if you're under sixteen. The best that can happen is that you'll be found and brought back home — probably by the police. By this time you'll be in trouble with your parents and the police.

Do not try to have a 'do-it-yourself' abortion. There are no pills you can get to give yourself and end your pregnancy. Boiling hot baths, drinking a bottle of gin or falling down stairs only produce third degree burns, big hang overs or broken necks. If any of these methods worked there would be no unwanted babies in the world. The two most dangerous things a girl can do are to try to abort herself or go to an illegal 'back street' abortionist. No one, not even a qualified doctor or nurse, can do an abortion legally or safely unless it's been arranged through the proper organisations (see page 115). You can end up killing yourself or being killed.

Some girls think about committing suicide. A few try it. But being pregnant is not the end of the world — you do have some choice and there are people to help you.

With some careful thought and planning it's possible to find the right solution for you. And within a few weeks or months the nightmare of an unwanted pregnancy can all be over. The first thing to realise is that you can't go through it all alone.

Who to tell

Almost certainly a girl is going to have to tell her parents in the end, especially if she's under 16. But it may help to talk to someone else first.

Boyfriend
The most natural person to tell is the boy involved, if you know who it is. Boys can react in many different ways. He may turn out to be the most kind and helpful friend in the world. Or he may turn out nasty and not want to know. Or he may panic more than the girl. If she is under sixteen, he has broken the law (see page 102). So when he hears that his girlfriend is pregnant, apart from being scared and worried, he may also have a vivid picture of himself in the arms of the law. The boy has no rights over you or the baby however much he might like to be a father.

Friend
A friend – especially one who has been through all this herself – can be a great help. An older friend, neighbour or relative may help tell your parents. But however close or good your friend might be, she or he won't necessarily know what to do any more than you do.

Teacher
There are some teachers who will do little more than throw up their hands in horror. But there are many who will be kind and helpful. The chances are that your form teacher will have a pretty good idea of what's up in any case. A sympathetic teacher can be a very good ally if you're expecting trouble at home. One of your parents' worries will be about your education. Your teacher should be able to help you with this problem.

Personnel Officer
Some factories and firms employ personnel staff to help their workers with problems such as this. You may want extra time off from work to get all the medical advice you'll need and the personnel officer should be able to help arrange this.

Professional advice
If a girl hasn't visited her doctor she'll have to quite soon. She'll need to get the medical attention that every pregnant woman needs, or to discuss the possibility of getting an abortion. An abortion has to be done quickly because after three months it is both dangerous and nearly impossible to get one. And it can take time to arrange.

There are various organisations a girl can go to for concrete help and advice. The law requires that the parents of a girl under 16 sign the consent form for an abortion operation. If you don't want your parents to know, say so and explain why. They'll still give you advice and help (including help on how to tell your parents). Most large towns have at least one of the organisations or clinics mentioned on page 115 you can go to. Phone them first to see if you need an appointment or have to pay a fee. Their advice is only 'professional' in the sense that it will be good and accurate, not bossy. They are informal and very friendly.

Parents
Your parents may be the best people in the world to tell once you've found the courage – or they may be the worst. But, in either case, if you live at home or are under 16 they'll have to be told. The chances are that their first reaction will be the same as yours – panic. If they didn't know you were having sex they may be very shocked. They might feel angry, hurt, disgraced, ashamed, or a mixture of all these things.

Their reactions can range from worrying about how your education will be affected to what the neighbours will think. If you have younger sisters and brothers they'll probably worry about whether they should be told. It's more than likely that a lot of things will get said which will later be regretted.

Parents can be surprising. Many will give you a lot of support. Some who for years have been warning their daughter that she'll get thrown out of the house if she ever gets pregnant turn out to be really kind and realistic. But they may not know what to do. If you have made the effort to contact an organisation which can help, your parents may realise that you're not as irresponsible as they thought. After all, for many girls getting pregnant is simply an accident.

It will help if you can try to understand how they feel and why. Hopefully they'll try to understand how you feel as well. One thing's certain: endless rows and discussions about how and why you got pregnant won't help at all. A decision on what to do has to be made — and soon.

Abortion

An abortion means that a doctor ends, or terminates, a pregnancy. It's a very controversial subject. There are those who campaign to make abortion free and available to every woman 'on demand' so that every child is a wanted child. Others are very much opposed to abortion and want to make it impossible or very much harder to get than it already is.

Those who are against abortion argue on religious and humane grounds that an unborn child, called a foetus (pronounced fee-tuss), has as much right to live as a born child. They point out that having an abortion can cause mental and physical complications for the pregnant woman. They say that unwanted babies give a lot of happiness to childless couples wanting to adopt. Some believe that many women are pressured into having an abortion because society does not make it easy for a single woman to keep her child.

Those in favour of abortion don't think it makes sense to talk of a foetus as a child until it's actually been born or until about twenty eight weeks after it was conceived, which is when it might just survive if it was born early. They point out that no method of birth control is one hundred per cent safe and that it's unfair to make women suffer just because their contraceptive failed. Unwanted and unplanned children can result in misery, poverty, battered babies, unhappy people or broken families.

The mental and physical complications which can follow from having a baby and then giving it away can be far greater than any complications which may result from having an abortion. Many women feel that they should have the right to control their own bodies and the number of children they have and that this should not be left up to (mostly male) scientists and politicians. They argue that if abortion is illegal it will mean that, once again, rich women will be able to get safe abortions but women without the money will be forced to have dangerous, back street abortions.

If you are thinking about having an abortion you'll probably be weighing up the arguments for and against – but you'll also be thinking of your own particular situation. Before you take your decision talk it over with your doctor or a counsellor at one of the pregnancy advisory services mentioned on page 115.

How Safe?

Whatever your feelings are it's important to get some facts straight. Any operation involves some risk, and an abortion is no exception. The sooner you have your abortion the safer it is. But is is actually safer to have an abortion than it is to be pregnant and have a baby. Out of every 100,000 women who have a legal abortion in one year, about four die. Out of every 100,000 women who continue in their pregnancy, about twelve die.

There are other possible complications both in having an abortion and in being pregnant. An abortion can cause an infected or damaged womb. Or it may cause your cervix to become so stretched that it makes it difficult to have a baby in the future. It can cause such heavy bleeding that a blood transfusion will be needed.

But these things can also happen to women who continue in their pregnancy, either by having a miscarriage (an accidental, spontaneous abortion), or while giving birth.

How to get an Abortion

According to the law you can get a legal abortion provided two doctors sign a form agreeing that one or more of the following things is true:

— to continue being pregnant would mean a greater risk to your life than to have an abortion.
— to continue being pregnant would mean a greater risk to your physical or mental health than to have an abortion.
— to continue being pregnant would involve a greater risk to the physical or mental health of any other children in your family than to have an abortion.
— there is reasonable suspicion that the child will be born seriously mentally or physically handicapped.

If you are under 16

You will need the written consent of your parents, guardians or your social worker if you are in care. The majority of girls under 16 get an abortion free on the National Health Service. No NHS doctor would agree to do an abortion without getting this written consent. If you go to one of the private charitable pregnancy advisory services listed on page 115 they will also need your parents' written permission but they are very sympathetic to the problems that many young girls have. Explain to the counsellor exactly what your personal situation and problem is.

Getting a free Abortion on the National Health Service

Go to you own doctor, and explain why you want an abortion. You'll be given an internal examination. Some doctors don't approve of abortion and will either refuse to sign the form or refuse to let you have it on the NHS. If you can afford to pay, your doctor may take the view that you should have it done privately to make room in hospital for a woman who can't afford an abortion. If your doctor does not agree to an abortion, the best plan is to go to a doctor at a non profit-making pregnancy advisory service centre (see page 115).

If your doctor agrees, she or he will arrange for you to see a gynaecologist who is a specialist in these matters, at a hospital. When you see the gynaecologist, explain to her or him why you want an abortion. You will be given an internal examination. You may be sent to a psychiatrist if the specialist wants to find out how your pregnancy is affecting your mental state. If the specialist agrees to an abortion you will be told when you can go into hospital. In the hospital you may find yourself in a ward with other women happily expecting babies and women who are trying to find out why they can't have babies at all; this can be very upsetting for everyone. Make sure you take plenty of magazines or books to take your mind off it all when you need to.

Arranging for an abortion is seldom just as easy as this. In some towns and areas it can be easier than in others, depending on how long the waiting list is for beds at hospitals and how sympathetic the health authority or individual doctors are. But if your doctors seem to be delaying, don't delay yourself. If you get to be ten week pregnant (ie. it is ten weeks since your last period) and you have no immediate date fixed for a hospital bed, go to one of the pregnancy advisory services to try and arrange for a private abortion (see page 115).

Private or Charitable Abortion Services

The organisations listed on page 115 all provide non-profit making advisory services. They charge as little as possible but you should expect to pay around £70.00. They can sometimes arrange a free NHS abortion even if you've already been refused one. They may be able to give you financial help such as an interest-free loan. If you belong to one of the private patient schemes like British United Provident Association (BUPA) or Private Patients Plus (PPP) you should be able to claim back the money.

Check on the phone beforehand whether you need an appointment. There's often a long queue. You'll have a talk with a counsellor and then be given an appointment to see a doctor. If the doctor agrees, you'll be booked into a clinic or nursing home which is specially licenced by the government to give abortions. Find out who and when you have to pay from the advisory service. You may not be allowed visitors, but the atmosphere is usually very friendly and nearly everyone is there for the same reason.

Commercial Abortion Services

There are a number of commercial pregnancy advisory services which give abortions at high prices in order to make a profit. They send women to private gynaecologists and private clinics, who also charge high fees. All clinics have to be licensed and the government occasionally removes the licence from a clinic or nursing home that doesn't come up to standard. If you are not sure if your advisory service or clinic is as cheap as it could be, or might not be properly licensed, phone the British Pregnancy Advisory Service to check (page 116).

Live in Northern Ireland?

Abortion is not legal in Northern Ireland and you can usually only get your pregnancy terminated for strictly medical reasons. Ulster Pregnancy Advisory Association Ltd (address, page 117) provides a counselling service and can then refer you to the British Pregnancy Advisory Service clinic in Liverpool. Many women go to England for the operation. If you decide to go to England, phone one of the charitable advisory services on page 115 before you leave to get a definite appointment. They won't be able to guarantee an abortion until they've seen you, but they'll probably make a provisional booking at a clinic or nursing home within a day or two of your first appointment so that you won't have to stay away from home too long.

Live in Eire?

Abortion is illegal in Eire, but many women do go over to England for a legal termination. The majority have to pay. The Irish Family Planning Association (address, page 115). is very sympathetic and helpful to girls who want a pregnancy termination operation.

Methods of abortion

These vary according to how many weeks pregnant you are.

First 3 days

There is a pill that some doctors will prescribe in extreme circumstances such as rape. This has very unpleasant side effects and should not be taken more than once or twice in a lifetime. It has to be taken within the first 3 days of pregnancy.

First 14 days

No one can be certain they're pregnant until their period is fourteen days late. But extraction, sometimes called interception, can be used to take out all the contents of the womb within the first fourteen days after unprotected intercourse. In America it's used for 'lunch-time' abortions – it only takes a couple of hours of your time. It's not yet widely available in Britain.

Up to 12 weeks

The most common method used is called vacuum aspiration. A thin flexible plastic tube called a cannula is pushed up the vagina, through the cervix and into the womb. The other end is attached to a suction machine which draws the contents of the womb out. You may stay in overnight, or you may be able to leave after a few hours if the clinic or hospital has an out-patient service.

12-16 weeks

At this stage you will be given a minor operation called a Dilation and Curettage (D and C). This is almost always done under a general anaesthetic. The cervix is stretched, (or dilated) and the contents of the womb are scraped out (or curetted). You'll stay in overnight.

After 16 weeks

Injections of salt solution or drugs can be used to make the womb contract so that it pushes out its contents. It creates a sort of mini-labour which can last several hours. You won't be given a general anaesthetic, but will be sedated so that you won't really be aware of what is happening. You stay in hospital for 2 or 3 days.

18-24 weeks

A hysterotomy (*not* a hysterectomy which means removal of the womb) is an operation which involves cutting through the abdomen and the wall of the womb to remove the contents. It leaves a scar and should only be done at a late stage of pregnancy if other methods are not possible. You have to stay in the hospital or clinic for about a week and 2-3 weeks convalescence is recommended afterwards.

After the abortion

Most women recover from their abortions very quickly. A general anaesthetic can leave you feeling quite tired for a day or two, but a little rest is all that's needed. Late abortions take longer to recover from. You may need a couple of days in bed. After a hysterotomy you should have a couple of weeks rest to recover fully.

It's normal to bleed and feel cramp pains for several days afterwards. Use a sanitary towel, not a tampon, because it's very easy to get an infection if you push anything up your vagina. Don't have intercourse for 6 weeks. Avoid energetic exercise for a couple of weeks – or longer if your doctor tells you. If you're at school and have to take part in sports, or if your job is very strenuous, ask the doctor who arranged the abortion to write a note to get you excused – no reason need be given. Don't go swimming for 6 weeks.

Most doctors, clinics and hospital arrange an appointment for a final check up 6 weeks after an abortion. It's important to keep this appointment because it's possible that there will be a complication, although the majority of girls don't have any complications at all. Go to your doctor, clinic or hospital if you get a fever, very bad cramps or if the normal bleeding that happens after an abortion lasts for longer than 10 days. If you suddenly start to bleed very heavily get immediate medical attention. You can expect your first period from 4 to 6 weeks afterwards. If it doesn't come by this time, go to your doctor. If you do get an infection it has to be treated quickly but can be quite easily cured with antibiotics.

Many women feel relieved after their abortion. It's also quite normal to feel rather sad or depressed either immediately after the abortion or a few months later when the baby would have been born. This may also be like the depression many women feel after childbirth. It's partly a result of the changing level of hormones that takes place in the body of every woman after she's been pregnant — a natural feeling and it does go away. Or it may be because at any other time, under different circumstances you would have liked a baby. Again, the feelings will pass.

If you do feel upset — you may feel angry, lonely or guilty — don't bottle it up. It often helps to talk about it with a friend, especially one who's been through it all herself. You might find it helpful to go to a women's centre if there's one in your area (see page 120) or talk to the doctor or counsellor who arranged your abortion.

Having a baby

If you're having a baby you have to make several decisions – among them whether to live with the father of the baby, or marry him, or neither. Our society doesn't make it easy for a single girl to be pregnant or for anyone to bring up a child on their own. But there's no reason why anyone should go through it literally on her own. You may get a lot of support from your parents. But they may not know what to do either. There are many organisations (see page 117) which exist for no other reason than to help young unmarried girls with the problems they may have to face when they're pregnant. *Remember*: don't go it alone – you don't have to. These organisations are there to help you, so contact them.

Where to stay

A big problem facing pregnant girls whose parents are too shocked or angry to help is finding somewhere to stay. Being lonely will only make your pregnancy all the worse especially if it's an unwanted pregnancy. Even if your parents are very upset, shocked or angry, unless you decide to live with the father of the baby, it is probably best in the long run if you can stay at home – especially if you're under 18. Failing that, see if you can stay with a sympathetic friend or relative. Many of the organisations mentioned on page 117 will help you find somewhere to stay if you have to leave home.

If you feel you need somewhere to stay in the last couple of months of your pregnancy and immediately after the baby is born you may be able to go to a mother and baby home or live with a family. To find out about these possibilities, contact the National Council for One Parent Families (page 118), or the social services department of your local council (outside the cities, the social services are run by County authorities). Look them up in the phone directory or ask at the Town Hall.

Leaving home

If things do get really bad at home many girls decide to leave. Probably one of the unkindest things they can do is just to take off and leave their parents to worry themselves sick about where they are and what's happening to them. It's always worth ringing home to let your parents know that you're at least alive and well.

If you're under 18, your parents can legally ask the authorities to find you and bring you home. If you are found and if the social services department of the local council decide you are in need of 'care and protection', they can apply for a Care Order. This means that you will appear in court and the magistrates may appoint a social worker to decide whether you should live at home or in a residential or foster home. A Care Order passed when you are under 16 lasts until you are 18; if you're over 16 it lasts until you are 19. You can apply to the court at any time for the order to be ended. To find out how to do this contact the National Council for Civil Liberties (page 113), Release (page 114) or ask at your local Citizen's Advice Bureau, (look up in phone book).

When you are pregnant and under a care order, the social worker is involved in deciding what to do about your pregnancy. If you're under 16 you can't get an abortion without the consent of the social services department. But you have the right to decide whether to keep the baby or have it adopted or fostered. If you have any complaints about or problems with the social services department, contact One Parent Families (page 118).

Medical care

It's very important for every pregnant woman to look after her health and have regular medical attention particularly by the time she's fifteen weeks pregnant. (That's 15 weeks after the day the last period started).

You can register with any doctor who's prepared to take you on to her or his 'panel'. You can get a list of doctors in the area where you're staying from the local post office. If the doctors you contact all seem to be full up, ask for advice at the Citizen's Advice Bureau. If your doctor doesn't offer a maternity service, she or he may send you to a doctor who does, or to a local clinic (called ante-natal clinics – ante-natal means before birth) which are often attached to hospitals.

If you're under 16 a doctor can't legally treat you without your parents' permission (except in emergencies). But much depends on what the doctor thinks: many believe that it is better to treat a young patient than to frighten them away and make them feel too scared ever to come for medical treatment.

You shouldn't be treated any differently whether you're married or single. At the clinic or hospital you'll probably be called 'Mrs' – the more enlightened ones will use just your first name. If you run into any problems about the way you're treated, contact One Parent Families or the National Patient's Association.

Some hospitals have a medical social worker attached to them who can help patients sort out their practical problems, such as where to stay, money, and personal worries.

Finding out about pregnancy and childbirth

Doctors and clinics usually have a mass of leaflets about all aspects of pregnancy – diet, exercise, welfare rights etc – so just ask for them. One Parent Families, the Family Planning Association and the National Childbirth Trust will answer any specific questions you have and they all produce many very helpful books and leaflets. Send for booklists.

Living together

If you are over 16 but under 18 you can live together as long as you have the permission of your parents or legal guardians. If they won't give their permission, they can prevent you from living together by making you a Ward of Court (which means that you have to get the permission of the court to live together) or you may be put into the care of the local authority.

The legal and practical advantages and disadvantages of living together and of getting married are set out very clearly in *Women's Rights: A Practical Guide*, by Anna Coote and Tess Gill (Penguin, paperback). You'll also find a lot of useful information on the subject in *The Single Woman's Guide to Pregnancy and Parenthood*, by Pat Ashdown-Sharp (Penguin, paperback). Both these books are very useful to both girls and boys.

Marriage

You can't get married until you're sixteen. If you live in England, Wales or Northern Ireland you need the written permission of your parents or legal guardians until you're 18 if you want to get married in a registry office. For a church ceremony you don't need any consent, provided the banns are read on three consecutive Sundays without objection. In Scotland, you don't need any permission once you're 16. In Eire you need permission up to the age of 21.

Traditionally, couples over 16 but under 18 who can't get permission have eloped to Scotland. Gretna Green, the town nearest to the English border has become famous for so-called 'shot-gun' marriages. But eloping to Scotland isn't such a very good idea. Scottish law insists that one or other of you live for at least 15 days in Scotland before you can marry. This usually gives parents and guardians enough time to make you a Ward of Court and a summons will be served on you telling you to appear in court. If you go ahead with the wedding, having received this summons, your marriage will still be legal but you may be prosecuted for contempt of court. This will mean that you'll have to attend a session in court for a legal ticking off. If you manage to get married without your parents' consent, by lying about your age, your marriage will still be legal (providing you're over 16) but you could be prosecuted for making a false statement.

In most cases it's probably best to stay put and apply directly to the court for permission to marry. You'll need to go to the Clerk's office at your local Magistrates Court or County Court (look up in phone book) to get the necessary forms. Once you've filled these in and sent them back to the court you'll be told of the time, place and date of the hearing. Your case will be held in private although your parents will be allowed in. All you have to do is tell the magistrate why you want to marry. To find out if you can get legal aid to pay the costs, get a form from any solicitor, the Citizens Advice Bureau or the nearest Law Society Legal Aid Area Office (look up in phone book).

Adoption & Fostering

Adoption means having your baby but then allowing it to be brought up by another family and giving up all your rights as a parent. Fostering means having your baby but then allowing it to be cared for either by another family or in a home, until you're able to look after it yourself.

Every mother has the right to decide for herself whether to keep her baby or have it adopted or fostered. The baby's father has no such rights. It's never an easy decision. You don't have to decide until after the baby is born but it's a good idea to try to work it out in your own mind before. Many women feel differently after the birth. You have to be very careful not to make an unrealistic decision at a time when you might be feeling very strongly either way. Don't try to work it all out on your own – and don't be pressured into doing what you don't want to do. It's a big step in anyone's life and you'll need as much moral support and sympathy as you can get. One Parent Families will give you all the advice, information and help you need on weighing up the argument for and against keeping your child, adoption or fostering. They won't put any pressure on you one way or the other. They'll also tell you about any similar organisations in your area.

Adoption and fostering can be arranged either through the social services department of your local council (look up in phone book) or through one of the organisations listed on page 117. The Association of British Adoption and Fostering Agencies (address, page 117) can also send you a list and advise you on agencies in your area.

Education

By law you have to be educated until you reach school-leaving age, which is 16. You may be able to stay on at your own school if you, your parents and the head teacher all agree. You may be able to transfer to another school nearby. In the past most schools used to expel any girl who became pregnant but many now have a more liberated and sympathetic approach. If you're under 16 and do leave school because you're pregnant, the local education authority has an obligation to make arrangements for a tutor to teach you at home or wherever you're staying. The minimum is 10 hours a week but you may be able to get extra teaching if you're taking exams. Some authorities, however, don't have enough teachers and many girls find it difficult to get enough tuition to bring them up to exam passing standards.

Similar arrangements can be made if you're over 16 and want to stay on at school or college. Your head teacher or the welfare officer of the local education authority (look up in phone book or ask at the Town Hall) can help you and your parents with any education problems. If you run into any difficulties contact One Parent Families (address, page 118) or the Advisory Centre for Education (address, page 114).

It may not be plain sailing but it is worth going on with your schooling. Getting pregnant shouldn't be a reason for giving up an education. Any girl who decides to keep her baby might well need the better money that often goes with a job that requires exam certificates, and it's never easy to pick up again once you've left off.

Work

A girl who has worked for the same employer for at least 2 years can't be sacked simply because she's pregnant. Any girl who has worked in the same job for less than 2 years but over 6 months and is sacked because she's pregnant may be able to take her case to the Tribunal for Unfair Dismissal. She will probably win her case unless her pregnancy has made it impossible to do her job (such as lifting very heavy loads etc) or if her job is too dangerous for a pregnant woman to do (such as working with X-rays or with certain chemicals). Some firms now give their workers paid leave for a month or two while they have their baby and just after, but they don't have to by law, so many don't. A few firms give their men workers paid leave while their wife or girlfriend has a baby.

Until the law makes it possible for women to insist on the right to maternity leave, and makes it impossible for firms to sack a worker just because she's pregnant, there's no doubt that many pregnant women will find themselves discriminated against. Obviously even if the law is not on their side, many firms will make life very unpleasant for someone they want to sack. This is certainly one area in which women still have to win some basic rights. In the meantime, anyone with work problems should try not to get too discouraged. In a time of high unemployment it's worth hanging on to your job until the last possible moment — but keep an eye open for any other jobs that might be going.

Anyone with problems about being sacked or getting time off for medical treatment can get advice from One Parent Families or the Equal Opportunities Commission (addresses, page 113).

Money

To find out about maternity grants, allowances, sickness, unemployment and supplementary benefits etc, contact the local Department of Health and Social Security (look up in phone book). The Citizens Advice Bureau will also be able to give help on this matter. If you're over 16 and either you or your husband have paid enough stamps you may be entitled to a maternity grant of £25. For a married woman there is a child benefit allowance of £2.50 per week once the baby is born. Unmarried mothers and fathers can claim an extra 50p per week. To claim these benefits and allowances you have to fill in various forms. Some of these forms are available from your local post office, others from the social security office. The post office should be able to tell you what to do, the Citizens Advice Bureau will help you fill them in. The Claimants Union (address, page 117) will also help you with information on what to claim for and how.

If you're at college you may be entitled to an extra allowance. To find out about this, contact One Parent Families (page 118).

Rights of the Father

A single mother is automatically her child's only legal guardian; the single father has no automatic rights over his child unless he gets them established in a court of law. It can be very difficult for a man to prove that he is the father of his child. If you want to take responsibility for your child and the mother refuses to let you, you will have to apply to the magistrates court. In court you have to prove that the mother accepted payments or gifts from you shortly after the baby was born and/or that she admitted that you were the father, perhaps in a letter or by telling people who you could then use as witnesses. A blood test to check out both your blood group and that of the baby can only prove that you are *not* the father of a child – it can't prove that you definitely are the father.

If the court decides that you are the father you will be responsible for supporting the child. If the mother of your child tries to prevent you from seeing your child you can apply to the Magistrates Court for 'right of access'. The court will probably rule that you should be allowed to see your child unless it decides that your character is so bad that it would be dangerous for the child if you did.

If you want to look after your child long term you will have to go to court and prove that the mother is incapable of looking after your child and that you are capable. In the past, courts have almost automatically assumed that a mother is better at looking after children than a father, however good he would be or however bad she might be at doing so. More and more courts are treating the mother and father as equals and deciding on the merits of each particular case – although most still decide in favour of the mother.

If you need any legal advice on the matter of paternity, contact a solicitor or One Parent Families (page 118).

Maintenance

If the father refuses to accept responsibility and the mother wants him to support the child financially, she has to take 'affiliation proceedings' against him. This means going to a Magistrates Court and proving that he really is the father. You can apply for an affiliation order before the baby is born or up to 3 years after. You can't apply if you are married to another man and are living with him. You don't *have* to claim maintenance from the father if you don't want to. If you are claiming social security, you may be under some pressure to accept maintenance because this means you get less money from the social security. You don't have to tell them who the father is or where he is.

Looking after our bodies

When we're young, parents are always telling us to clean our teeth, scrub our nails and wash behind our ears, probably until we're sick of it. But little mention, if any, is made of how we should look after our sex organs. As a result, some of us don't take enough care and others worry too much. It's as important to tell the difference between healthy and unhealthy sex organs as it is for any other part of the body. If we don't keep them clean they can get infected and will need medical treatment.

A healthy vagina naturally produces a small amount of clear or slightly milky secretion and some oils to keep the sensitive skin soft and moist. If a girl doesn't wash her sex organs every day they will get musty and sweaty like any other part of her body.

Under the foreskin of an uncircumcised penis a white wax-like secretion called smegma is produced naturally. A circumcised penis may also produce traces of this smegma. If this is not washed away every day it starts to smell unpleasant.

All you need to keep your sex organs clean is soap and water. The jokes about cunts that smell like fish and cocks that smell like overripe cheese don't help in making us feel confident that our sex organs ever smell good. But when they're healthy the smell is fresh and pleasant. Don't be taken in by adverts for vaginal deodorants or heavily scented soaps and powders. In order to sell their products, manufacturers would have us believe us believe that our sex organs are naturally 'dirty' and that their natural smell is 'offensive'. It's simply not true.

There are some basic rules to keep your sex organs clean and healthy:

— wash your sex organs and bottom every day
— wipe your bottom from front to back
— after sex, wash your sex organs thoroughly
— any contraceptive, such as the cap, which is to be used again must be washed well
— don't put anything into your vagina or anus that you think might have germs on it

Sexually transmitted diseases (STDs)

Even the most hardened of people can usually find sympathy for someone who is ill. But when it comes to illnesses that are caught and spread by having sex, reactions are most likely to be 'serves you right for being dirty', or 'she/ he must be putting it around a lot'. The reasons for these attitudes probably has much to do with people's feelings about sex. If you don't think sex is a normal part of life (which it certainly is) or if you think that sex with more than one person during your whole life is wrong (which it certainly needn't be), then it's easy to see why you're going to think of a sexually transmitted disease as some sort of 'divine punishment' for being 'abnormal', 'dirty' or 'naughty'. No illness is a punishment. And a sexually transmitted disease (STD) is not caught by being dirty or by having sex with a great number of different people. You get it by having sex with one person who is infected with the disease.

The term 'sexually transmitted disease' covers a number of illnesses. There are some like syphilis (pronounced siff-ill-iss) and gonorrhoea (pronounced 'gon-or-rear') which can *only* be caught by having sex with someone who already has it. There are others like thrush, trich. and warts which you can get in this way but which you can also get without ever having had sex with anyone at all. They're a bit like colds – you can catch one if you have sex with someone who happens to have a cold but not everyone with a cold catches it by having sex!

Cure

Every so often the papers print an alarming horror story about some new strain of syphilis or gonorrhoea that can't be cured. Not true. Sometimes a certain strain is discovered to be more resistant to the available medicines but they can all be cured – they just need bigger doses than usual.

If you suspect you have any of the infections described in this chapter you must get immediate medical treatment. There's no point in hoping that if you do nothing it will go away. Sometimes there are no symptoms or the symptoms do go away. But this does NOT mean the disease has gone away. If they're not treated promptly, some of these diseases can have very serious consequences.

Where to get treatment

Treatment of some STDs need specialised medical knowledge and facilities which your own doctor probably won't have. You need to go to a Special Clinic. These aren't all the grim places they once were. You can go straight to any Special Clinic for free advice and treatment. You don't need a letter from your doctor or an appointment.

All treatment is absolutely confidential. Treatment centres for STDs have different names. The following are in use throughout the UK: Special Clinic,

88

Department of Genito-Urinary Medicine, Department of Venereology, STD Clinic, Department of Genital Medicine.

To find out where your nearest Special Clinic is and what its opening hours are: look for posters in public lavatories, health centres, or post offices. Look in the telephone directory under the various headings mentioned above. Some areas have recorded telephone messages, which give information about symptoms and clinics. Phone or visit the Casualty Department of your local hospital or a local doctor and ask for the address of your local clinic. The Citizens Advice Bureau will also tell you.

Take a friend along with you if you can't face the prospect of going on your own. You'll be given a number – partly because so many people give a false name and address, and also so that your name won't be yelled out across the waiting room when it's your turn. But you should also give your correct name and address in confidence to avoid all confusion.

Be prepared to tell the doctor:

- what symptoms you've had (if any) and for how long
- what sex partners (if any) you've had in the past 3 months and whether you can find them again
- some specific details about the sort of sexual contact you've had (if any) – whether you've had oral, anal, or homosexual sex
- if you're allergic to any drugs

Persevere if you meet an unsympathetic doctor – the information is important.

Be prepared

- to undress and have an examination of your sex organs
- to give a sample of pee
- to have a blood test on your first visit (this involves a relatively painless jab in your arm or bottom)

Some smear samples will be taken and examined under a microscope while you wait in the clinic. For a girl, smears will be taken from the neck of her womb inside her vagina, from her anus and from her throat. For a boy, a smear is taken by gently pushing a tiny platinum loop a little way into the hole in the tip of his penis. This may sound horrific but he'll hardly feel a thing. Try to relax. Smears will also be taken from his anus and throat. Some samples will be looked at under the microscope while you wait. Others will go to a laboratory and results will be known only after several days.

Remember:

- the first visit may take up to an hour because the doctor will do a physical examination
- you may have to go back for more visits before correct treatment is given
- you may need to take time off school, college or work. If so, you can ask

for a doctor's certificate of attendance. (This won't state the reasons why you're at the hospital or clinic)
— whatever happens in the clinic is confidential and not told to anyone else even if they should try to find out
— you don't have to give your age
— do not have sex with anyone until you've been told that you are completely cured
— once you have been cured you can catch the infection again if you have sex with someone who is infected

Contact tracing

There has been a vast increase in STDs — gonorrhoea has reached epidemic proportions over the last ten years. If everyone with an STD went for treatment and told their sex partners that they might be infected, and then they also went for treatment, the diseases would soon disappear. But too many people feel too ashamed or guilty to admit it to anyone — sometimes even to themselves. To try to prevent the spread of the more serious STDs (gonorrhoea and syphilis) many area health authorities like to trace all those who have had sex with an infected person. This is why some clinics ask for the names of those you've had sex with. They then, very discreetly (or no one would ever give them any names) get in touch with everyone who might have caught the disease. Their hope is that they will get in touch with contacts before they have sex with anyone else and so spread the disease even further.

You don't have to give the clinic any names if you don't want to. But if you decide not to, you *must* yourself tell everyone you think could have caught the disease from you. If you don't, and they never discover that they have the disease, they may not only give it to someone else but they and many more besides could become seriously ill and possibly end up unable to have babies — or dead.

Venereal diseases (VD)

The term 'venereal' comes from the word Venus — goddess of love — which may sound like a bad joke to anyone with VD. The law defines three STDs as VD — gonorrhoea, syphilis and soft sore. Soft sore (or chancre — pronounced shanker) is now almost wiped out but gonhorrhoea and syphilis are very common.

You *cannot* catch VD from toilet seats, door knobs, dirty plates, clothes, towels, from water you've been swimming in, or in any way other than from direct sexual contact with someone — of the opposite or same sex — who has caught the disease. Direct sexual contact can be in one or more of the following ways:
— sexual intercourse (between penis and vagina)
— genital contact (between vagina and vagina)
— anal contact (between penis and anus)
— oral contact (between sex organs and mouth)

Sexually transmitted diseases are very
easy to pick up and to spread around

Gonorrhoea (also known as the clap or a dose)
This is the most common type of VD. It's much more serious than most people realise. The tiny organism that causes gonorrhoea is called a gonoccocus. It dies within a few seconds of being out in the air and lives only inside the warmth and moistness of the internal organs. Signs of gonorrhoea, if there are any, start to appear 2 to 10 days after the germs have been picked up.

Symptoms
The symptoms of gonorrhoea are different for females and males. In women there are often no symptoms at all. In men the symptoms are usually obvious.

91

In women:
- sometimes there is an unusual discharge – often yellowish – from the vagina
- sometimes a burning feeling when peeing
- sometimes fever, chill, pains in the stomach and joints
- sometimes an infection in the anus causing discharge and irritation

In men:
- pain when peeing
- yellow discharge leaking from the penis
- sometimes infection in the anus causing irritation and a discharge

Treatment

If it's not treated, whether or not there are any symptoms, the gonorrhoea germs will spread to the rest of the internal sex organs and cause inflammation. Eventually this can mean that it will be impossible ever to have a baby.

Treatment is simple: one or more injections of penicillin or other antibiotics in your bottom or thigh is all that's needed to cure gonorrhoea. You must go back to the clinic to check that it's been completely cured.

Syphilis (also known as the pox or bad blood)

This is an extremely serious disease. It can kill you if it's left untreated. The tiny organism that causes syphilis is called a spirochete (pronounced spi-ro-keet). The first signs usually appear 3 to 6 weeks after you've caught the disease.

Symptoms

These are the same for women and men. They're not always easy to detect.

First stage: A painless sore which looks like a spot, blister or cold sore usually appears on or near the sex organs. It could be near the mouth. If it appears inside the anus or vagina it probably won't be noticed. The sore goes away after a few days or weeks.

Second stage: The germs spread through the blood stream to every part of the body. Within a few weeks they can cause a copper-coloured skin rash anywhere on the body (not to be confused with acne on the face), fever, sore throat, swollen glands and loss of hair. These symptoms go away eventually.

Third stage: This is a hidden stage which can last for many, many years. There are no signs but the germs are busy attacking all the organs of the body – the heart, lungs, eyes, nervous system, brain etc.

Final stage: Syphilis weakens, damages and cripples almost every organ in the body. It eventually causes paralysis, blindness, madness and/or death.

A pregnant woman with untreated syphilis can pass the disease into the blood stream of her baby so that it is born dead or diseased.

Treatment

Syphilis can be detected in its early stage by taking a smear from the sore. After the sore has disappeared it can only be detected in a blood sample.

Longer treatment is needed to cure syphilis than to cure gonorrhoea. Several injections of penicillin or some other drug are necessary. It can be completely cured in all stages, but if left to the last stages the damage done to the organs cannot be repaired.

Vaginal infections

A healthy vagina naturally produces a small amount of clear or milky non-smelling discharge. In between periods many girls have a slightly thicker and yellowish discharge – it's the discarded yellow body being discharged from the womb. A vaginal infection usually means that the discharge smells very bad indeed, is a dark yellow, white, grey or greenish colour and makes you want to scratch all the time right inside your vagina. Germs find the vagina a good place to grow in because it is warm and moist.

Vaginal infections come into the category of STDs which aren't necessarily caused by having sex, although they can be picked up by having sex with someone who has the infection. Other things that can cause vaginal infections include: feeling generally run down or ill, taking the birth control Pill.

If you have a vaginal infection, go to your doctor, who will prescribe you some drugs to clear it up and possibly some pessaries that look like big pills which you put up your vagina to stop the itching.
The following may help:

– keep your vagina as dry as possible – don't soak in hot baths
– don't scratch! This only makes it worse
– check whether you've left a tampon inside your vagina. If you have, take it out and have a good wash, but still go to your doctor
– wear cotton pants and avoid nylon underwear, tights and tight trousers
– wash and thoroughly dry your vagina after you have been to the toilet
– don't use tampons
– don't have sex (or if you don't want to give up sex, use a sheath)
– don't stop treatment when symptoms disappear – the full course of treatment is *very important*
– tell your sex partners – they may be infected and need treatment

Yeast Infection (also called Thrush, Candidosis or Monilias Yeast Infection) Yeast or fungus grows normally in the vagina, but is kept under control by the acid content of the natural secretions. If your system is thrown off balance the yeast starts to grow uncontrollably. It produces a thick white discharge which looks like cottage cheese and smells like baking bread. It makes you feel very itchy inside and can make it painful to pee. If you get thrush often and have a regular sex partner, make him go to the doctor to check whether he has thrush growing under his foreskin. Babies can pick up thrush which infects their eyes, so be very careful if there are any children around. Treatment is in the form of vaginal tablets and cream. Sometimes tablets are taken by mouth as well. Some antibiotics cause thrush.

Trichomoniasis (pronounced Trik-o-monnyassis, also called Trich or TV) Trich. is a tiny microbe which can be found in both women and men. There may be no symptoms at all. Usually there is a yellowish-green or greyish thin foamy discharge. This smells horrible and causes a sore feeling inside the vagina and on the external sex organs as well. It can often cause an infection in the bladder which makes peeing painful. It is usually caused by having sex with someone who has the infection – but not always. A girl can become infected if her vagina comes into close contact with a toilet seat, flannel or some other object used by an infected person.

Half of all the women who have Trich. also have gonorrhoea. Curing Trich. does not mean that you have been cured of gonorrhoea. Go to the Special Clinic to check for gonorrhoea.

Treatment is in the form of tablets taken by mouth.

Non-specific vaginitis

When doctors aren't sure exactly what is causing a discharge they call the infection non-specific. Any unusual discharge which may be white, yellow, green, grey or streaked with blood should be reported to your doctor. The first sign of an infection may be either a discharge or pain when you pee. These infections may be caused by having sex with someone who is already infected – but not always.

Treatment usually involves pessaries to put into the vagina and a cream to stop any itching.

Other infections and illnesses

Urethritis

This is an inflammation that men get in the tube running from the bladder to the tip of the penis. It has many different names and any of the following may be used by doctors or in the Special Clinic:

— NSU: Non-Specific Urethritis
— NGU: Non-Gonococcal Urethritis
— PGU: Post-Gonococcal Urethritis

All three terms are used to describe urethritis when the germ causing the infection hasn't been discovered by laboratory tests. NGU means that gonorrohea is not the cause of the symptoms. PGU means that the infection has been found in a man who has recently been cured of gonorrhoea. It is possible that urethritis was caught at the same time as gonorrhoea, but it isn't cured by the same drugs. It isn't possible to discover urethritis until the gonorrhoea has been cured.

Urethritis is more common than gonorrhoea. The symptoms are the same: discharge from the penis and pain when peeing. It's usually spread from person to person by sexual intercourse, but not always. It is sometimes possible for NSU to occur in a man even though he and his partner have intercourse only with each other, and his partner hasn't got it.

94

It's important that samples of the discharge from the penis are examined at the Special Clinic under a microscope and by laboratory tests so that hopefully the infection is accurately identified and the correct treatment is given. Penicillin, which is the usual treatment for gonorrhoea, does not cure NSU. Other antibiotics will be given.

Pubic lice (also called crabs or nits)

These unpleasant tiny creatures like to live in the pubic hair around the sex organs – but can get into the hair on other parts of the body as well. They suck blood and lay their eggs called nits that look like white blobs at the roots of hairs. They give you an itch which almost drives you mad! You can't wash them away however hard you try. They have to be killed by a chemical solution which you can buy over the counter without a prescription at any chemist.

You can also get these preparations from a special clinic or from your doctor on prescription.

You can catch crabs either from coming into close physical contact with someone who already has them, or from bedding, clothes, towels or even a toilet seat which has recently been used by someone with crabs.

Whether your hair is clean or dirty, crabs aren't fussy – they just want to suck your blood. Don't have sex with anyone until you're absolutely sure that there is not one nit left. It usually takes about a week to get rid of them. Wash all the sheets, towels and underwear that you've used and don't let anyone else use them until the crabs have disappeared.

Scabies (also called the Itch)

The Scabies itch is caused by a very tiny mite which burrows under the skin, particularly between the fingers, around the waist and in the armpits. Like crabs, these mites are very itchy.

You can catch scabies by having sex with someone who already has it, and by holding hands or using the clothes or towels or beds of someone who has it.

To cure scabies you need to buy a special lotion from over the counter at the chemists. Take a bath and spread the lotion over your body. Don't wash for twenty-four hours. Repeat 4 or 5 days later. Thoroughly wash your underclothes and sheets. Don't have any close contact with anyone until the scabies has gone.

Genital Herpes (pronounced her-pees)

The most common type of herpes is the cold sore that some people get on their lips. No one is completely sure how the herpes virus reaches the sex organs but it's thought that it's usually passed on by sexual intercourse or contact with the vagina, anus or mouth of an infected person.

The sores on the sex organs can be very uncomfortable and painful and there may be some discomfort when peeing. Some people also suffer from

95

painful lumps in the groin near the sex organs. The sores can become infected.

Treatment varies. No known antibiotic kills the virus but the clinic or your doctor may be able to prescribe some ointment that can relieve the pain and help healing.

Genital warts

Warts on or near the sex organs are caused by a virus. They look like common skin warts. They are usually sexually transmitted – but not always. The warts appear 1 to 9 months after coming into contact with the source of infection. Removal needs special treatment and is usually done in the Special Clinic.

Cystitis

This is an infection of the bladder and its outlet tube, the urethra. It's caused by a variety of illnesses and infections and is often difficult to diagnose. Cystitis after intercourse is very common (it's sometimes called 'honeymoon disease') but is not always due to an infection; it can be caused by the bruising of the bladder or urethra by the penis through the walls of the vagina. The symptoms are a painful, sometimes incredibly painful, burning-like feeling when peeing, and the urge to pee very often, even though there's only a very small amount. Sometimes there can be blood or pus in the pee.

It's a very common illness and probably as many as half of all women suffer from it at some time or other in their lives. Some women suffer repeated attacks. It can be sexually transmitted if the infection occurs from sexual intercourse causing a bladder infection.

Sometimes the infection can spread to the kidneys and this makes it a more serious illness. Because of the risk to the kidneys, everyone who gets the symptoms should go to their doctor for advice. This is especially important for girls under 15 whose kidneys are still growing.

Your doctor will check the type of germs causing the infection from a sample of your pee which you'll be asked for at the surgery. Antibiotics or drugs called sulphonamides may be prescribed to kill the germs. You may need an X-ray to see if there is any kidney damage. While tests are being done the following will help:

– keep up a good flushing-through effect by drinking at least 5 pints of water every day
– pee frequently – at least 6 times a day
– one bath a day is not enough. Keep a special flannel to wash round the entrance to the urethra each morning and evening and after you've been to the toilet. Don't use strong soaps, deodorants, antiseptics, creams or powder
– if your symptoms are related to sexual intercourse and you get an attack regularly sometime during the 48 hours after intercourse you may prevent attacks by the following: both partners wash their sex organs before inter-

course with cool water: dry gently: use a lubricant such as KY Jelly to prevent soreness and bruising: the girl should go to the toilet preferably 15 minutes before intercourse and definitely within 15 minutes after intercourse
— if an attack starts, drink half a pint of water every 20 minutes. Each hour for 3 hours take a level teaspoon of bicarbonate of soda which will help lessen the burning feeling. Keep warm, and wash your vaginal area front to back after every visit to the toilet. After these 3 hours the attack should have lessened sufficiently for you to go to your doctor

You can find out more about cystitis from the U & I Club which was specially set up to help women who get this illness (address, page 114).

A tight foreskin

Many small boys with an uncircumcised penis have a tight foreskin which makes it difficult and painful to draw it back over the head of the penis. It usually gets looser in time. If it is still tight by the time a boy is 12, he must go to a doctor who may circumcise him. This is a minor, painless operation which could involve a couple of days in hospital. He should *not* try to force it back himself.

Foreskin infections

Smegma, which is the wax-like secretion produced under the foreskin, urine and semen can collect under the foreskin and become infected if the penis is not washed carefully and regularly. When infected the foreskin becomes red, swollen, itchy and it produces pus. Your doctor will prescribe you something to cure this infection.

Blood from the penis

Streaks of blood in your semen or pee could be nothing more serious than a small burst blood vessel. But go to your doctor to check that it's nothing more serious.

Discharge from the penis

Most infections of the bladder which cause a discharge and pain when peeing are called 'Non-specific urethritis' (see also Thrush and Trich. on page 93). Sometimes, but not always, these infections are caused by having sex with someone who is infected. Your doctor will prescribe drugs to cure the infection.

Only one ball

When a baby boy is born he sometimes has only one ball or no balls at all showing. This is because the testicles, which start off inside the body, don't always go down into the bag of skin or scrotal sacs. He will need an operation before he is five or the undescended testicle or testicles won't grow properly. Occasionally a ball can slip back up into the groin and seem to disappear. If this happens — and it's quite common — go to your doctor who will be able to press it down into its proper place quite painlessly. Do not try to do this yourself.

Pain in testicles

Testicles are a very sensitive and vulnerable part of the body – as any boy who has been hit or kicked in the balls will know. There are several causes of pain in the balls. It can be caused by feeling sexually excited for a long time without reaching an orgasm. Ejaculating – either by masturbating or by sexual intercourse – should ease this pain. If the pain stays or gets very intense, go to your doctor to check whether it's something more serious.

A very sharp knock on the balls doesn't just hurt, it can also damage them. Never play cricket or any other game where there is a danger of getting your balls knocked without wearing a box to protect them.

Periods

Most women feel some pain or discomfort just before, during or just after their periods. This is often much worse when a young girl starts having periods. The symptoms can include: stomach cramps, diarrhoea, constipation, swollen breasts, sore breasts, a general all-over feeling of swollenness, a sudden bursting into tears for no apparent reason, irritability, feverishness, a rise in temperature, or feeling low and depressed. The lucky ones feel nothing – or hardly anything – at all, while the very unlucky ones feel so bad that they have to take to their beds for a few days.

Many women suffer a great deal from some or all these pains and illnesses but put up with them because they think they're inevitable. They needn't be. There's absolutely no point in putting up with any pain that could be cured just because it's 'the time of the month'.

A painkilling pill can sometimes relieve some of the pain and discomfort. You can buy them from any chemist. A little extra light exercise can also help lessen the cramps. Many women find it helps to hold a hot water bottle to their stomachs or to have a bath.

If the pains get unbearable go to your doctor. Or if you find you're extremely tense just before a period, this can also be controlled by pills. Your doctor may be able to prescribe hormone pills which will regulate your periods and ease the pain. They may also make your periods much lighter. (These pills are in fact exactly the same as birth control pills, which can produce painful side effects themselves, see page 57).

Having a period doesn't – and shouldn't – mean that a girl has to stop doing anything she normally does. She can still go swimming (plunging into coldish water usually stops the flow for a while), wash her hair, play games, have hot baths and have sex if she wants to.

Don't be tempted to use your period as an excuse to get out of doing something – unless you feel really rotten. It makes people think that girls who do genuinely feel very bad are just shamming.

Cancer

If it is discovered early enough, cancer can be cured in the majority of cases. Sadly, not everybody realises this and perhaps because the very thought of

98

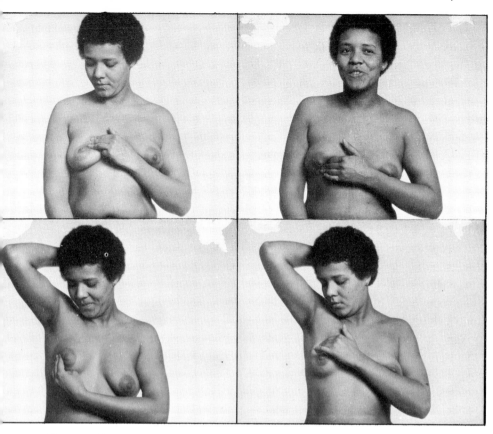

Breast self-examination: Get into the habit of checking your breasts regularly for any early signs of breast cancer

cancer is so terrifying, many people don't go for the necessary treatment at the stage when it could be cured.

Cancer occurs when some cells in some part of the body start to multiply in a wild and uncontrollable way. Eventually the cancerous cells get into the blood stream and travel to other parts of the body. If it is to be cured, it must be discovered before this spread is allowed to happen.

Breast cancer: Both women and men can get breast cancer although it's more frequently found in women. Girls should get into the habit of making regular examinations of their breasts. The best time to do this is just after a period has finished, perhaps in the bath or lying down.

What you do is this: examine the right breast thoroughly with your left hand. Massage the whole breast deeply in a circular fashion with the flat of the pads of the three middle fingers. Change the position to examine the left breast with your right hand. When you first begin to check your breasts, the natural and normal masses in them may scare you and you may fear you have breast cancer. But regular self-examination of the breasts after each period will soon make you familiar with the normal masses and then, when an abnormal lump appears, you can have it checked immediately by a doctor.

Things to look out for:

— any unusual lumps or thickening of the tissues inside
— a discharge from the nipple
— nipples that point in different directions
— an unusual pain or feeling of discomfort
— a nipple that appears to have withdrawn back into the breast. (Some girls and boys are born with nipples like this — called inverted nipples — so it's not necessarily a sign of cancer. A girl with nipples like this will need medical attention if she ever wants to breastfeed a baby)

If you discover any of these signs, go to your doctor immediately. DON'T wait, hoping they'll go away. You may not have cancer — a lump could be a harmless cyst that won't need any medical treatment. But it might be cancer and you can't afford to waste any time.

Cancer of the neck of the womb: also called cervical cancer or cancer of the cervix. Doctors think that there are several factors which can make getting cancer of the neck of the womb more likely. To decrease the chances, some doctors suggest that young couples having sex should use either the sheath or cap (plus spermicide) as a method of birth control. These are not the safest ways of preventing pregnancy but they do prevent the penis from coming into direct contact with the cervix and this seems to lessen the chances of getting cancer of the cervix.

A clean penis is also very important. Every boy, especially if he is not circumcised, must wash his penis regularly to prevent the spread of any infections.

It usually takes five or more years for cervical cancer to develop, but it can be detected and treated at an early stage before there is any real danger. A girl who starts to have sex at 16 or earlier must go to her family doctor or clinic to be tested for possible cancer of the cervix by the time she is 20. If your doctor can't do the test she or he will refer you to a clinic that can. Some Family Planning Association clinics carry out these tests, which are called Pap tests, cervical smear tests or cyto tests. The test involves an internal examination with the girl lying on her back with her legs spread apart. A few cells will be gently scraped from the cervix with a small spatula or swab of cotton wool. This is a very simple test — it doesn't hurt in the slightest.

If there is any change in the normal pattern of cell structure this will be discovered under a microscope in a laboratory. It can take a week or so for the results to be known. If there is a change in the cell structure a minor operation under a general anaesthetic will be arranged at a hospital. It usually means a day or two in hospital. The surgeon will cut out a small area from the cervix about the size of a thumb nail. This will not affect a girl's sex life or prevent her from having babies.

Whatever the outcome of the first test, and whether or not she's ever had sex, every girl should have a smear test at least every five years. A girl who is having sex regularly must have a smear test more frequently – her doctor or clinic will tell her how often. Remember: having sex doesn't *cause* cancer but it can in some cases increase a girl's chances of getting it. There are almost certainly many other reasons why a girl might get cancer of the cervix.

Cancer of the penis or testicles: This is fairly rare. Like all cancers, it must be treated in its early stages if it is to be cured. Any inflammation, difficulty in peeing, discharge, swelling, lump, spot or pain in the penis or balls should be reported to the doctor as soon as it's noticed. A lump in the balls is often just a rupture or a cyst. But whatever the cause, only a doctor will be able to tell. Don't waste any time – go to your doctor.

Sex and the law

Most of our laws are made to protect people from being harmed in one way or another. That's why we have laws against speeding or theft, for example. But when it comes to sex, although there are some laws which do try to protect us from being harmed by a sexual experience, the basic idea behind many of them seems to be that all sexual activity is bad unless it's between a married couple in order to have a baby. Even if the law doesn't spell this out, it is the way it often seems to work in practice. Such an old fashioned view of sex needn't matter to most people. But for some people it does. The law does occasionally interfere in people's sex lives, discouraging them from enjoying sex in the way they want to enjoy it and making them feel guilty, even when no one is going to be harmed.

The following explanations about some of our laws concerning sex and young people will give you an idea of how they work and the extent to which they affect our sex lives. If you need more detailed information about any of them, contact one of the relevant organizations listed at the end of the chapter.

Age of consent (Unlawful sexual intercourse)

A man or boy commits a crime if he has sexual intercourse with a girl who is under the age of consent. In England, Scotland and Wales, this age is 16. In Northern Ireland it is 17. In Eire it is 18. It doesn't matter whether or not the girl agreed and wanted to have intercourse. The girl doesn't commit a crime. The term 'age of consent' refers to the age when a girl is considered by the law to be old enough to agree to have sexual intercourse.

In practice the law works as follows:
— *If he is under 14* he can't be prosecuted.
— *If she is under 13* and he is over 14, it's a serious crime. He won't be able to defend himself by claiming he thought she was older.
— *If he is under 24* and she is between 13 and 15, he may be able to claim in court that he thought she was older.
— *If he is over 24*, the risk of prosecution and conviction increases.

Sentences vary vastly. If the boy is under 17 he won't be sent to prison but he may be placed in the care of the local authority. If he is over 17 he can get up to two years in prison. If the girl is under 13 the sentence could mean life (25 years).

A woman or girl can't be accused of unlawful sexual intercourse. But if the boy is under 16 she can be found guilty of indecent assault which carries a penalty of up to two years imprisonment.

For a boy to be taken to court for unlawful sexual intercourse, a complaint has to be made to the police. This can be made by anyone – it's usually made by the girl's parents. The police then decide whether or not to go ahead with the prosecution. Because this law is thought by many people to be very unfair (Why should boys or men be prosecuted but not girls? Does it make sense for it to be illegal to have sex on the day before her sixteenth birthday but not at one minute past midnight on her birthday?) quite often the police decide not to prosecute.

A boy who finds himself taken to court for unlawful sexual intercourse will need a solicitor. (see page 112). A girl under sixteen and who is – or thinks she is – pregnant or has a sexually transmitted disease, may find herself under some pressure to reveal the name of the boy involved. It's very unlikely for a doctor or social worker to make a complaint to the police, but this has happened. If she wants to protect the boy from the law she'll have to refuse to give his name. But if she does this she might be accused of having sex with so many boys that she doesn't know who the father is: if she is thought to be 'promiscuous', if her parents, teacher, police or social worker think that she is in 'moral danger' she could find herself in court and put into the care of the local authority, even though she has not broken the law.

Anal intercourse (buggery, or sodomy)

Many couples enjoy anal intercourse (which means the penis is put into the anus) without ever realising that it's illegal. It is no longer illegal for men to do it with each other in England and Wales as long as it's in private and they're both over 21. It is still illegal for male gays in Scotland, Northern Ireland and Eire.

Between heterosexuals, for a man to be prosecuted for buggery, the woman involved has to make a complaint to the police. It's still sometimes used as a reason for divorce (the papers sometimes call it an 'unnatural practice'). Buggery scenes are usually cut out of films before they reach the cinemas.

Bestiality (sex with an animal, zoophilia)

Some people feel sexually attracted to animals. It's not against the law to kiss, masturbate or be masturbated by an animal. But it is illegal for a woman or a man to have intercourse or buggery with an animal. It's totally impossible for a woman to get pregnant by having sex with an animal – or for an animal to get pregnant by having sex with a man.

Exhibitionism

Exhibitionists – also called flashers – get sexually aroused by exposing their sex organs to strangers. They're mostly men, although there are also women exhibitionists, who are unable to get aroused in any other way.

For any girl, being exposed to can be very upsetting and it's only natural to feel scared and angry – it's never nice to have an unwanted sexual experience or to be reminded that in our society many people think of women as sex objects. Also young girls aren't always sure what an exhibitionist's intentions are, and can be frightened by this. In fact very few exhibitionists ever want to harm or even touch the person they're exposing themselves to. Most are impotent and unable to get an erection when it comes to close contact with anyone.

Most doctors and sex therapists see exhibitionism as a symptom of a person's inability to relate to other people, but indecent exposure is a crime, and any exhibitionist who is reported to the police and then convicted can get up to 3 months in prison for a first offence and 12 months for any further convictions.

Homosexuality

Homosexuality is not a crime in England and Wales any more. It is a crime in Scotland, Northern Ireland and Eire for men to have homosexual relationships. Female homosexuality – lesbianism – has never been considered illegal. This may be because when laws about homosexuality were made in the last century women weren't considered capable of having loving and sexual feelings for one another – and it may have been a whole lot cheaper and more convenient for rich people to put their young maids and cooks together in the same bed! It's said that when Queen Victoria was presented with the outline of a law to make female homosexuality illegal her amazement and horror were so great that the politicians hastily dropped all the clauses. But wherever you live, being gay is not easy and male gays are still discriminated against in law, in ways that heterosexuals don't have to put up with. These are some of the differences:

- the age of consent for male gays living in England and Wales is 21. (For everyone else it is 16)
- gays are only allowed to have sex 'in private'. This means that no one else can be in the same room or flat – even if they all want to be there. (There is no such law for heterosexuals who are free to have group sex with any number of people).
- boys under 21 who have sex with an older man commit a crime. (Girls under 16 do not.)
- homosexual acts are still illegal for English and Welsh men who are members of the armed services or who are in the Merchant Navy.

104

If you need legal advice about homosexuality, contact the Campaign for Homosexual Equality (England and Wales) or any of the organisations listed on page 118).

Incest

Incest means having sexual intercourse with someone you know is your mother, father, brother, sister, grandmother or grandfather. It is considered to be a serious crime with a maximum punishment of 7 years in prison. If the girl involved is under thirteen, the punishment can be 25 years.

Incest is not particularly uncommon — especially between sisters and brothers, when it can be a loving sexual relationship. But many people find the thought of incest very upsetting and they feel angry about it. It used to be thought that any baby born as a result of an incestuous relationship would be mentally retarded or deformed in some way. In fact, this is not very likely. But any pregnancy which is the result of incest is always treated as reasonable grounds for an NHS abortion.

It obviously isn't easy for a young girl or boy to be able to say no to a father or mother or any older relative who wants to have intercourse with with them. That's because relationships between parents and children are not equal, and parents are likely to have much more control and power over the situation than their children. Nor is it easy for a young person to decide whether to report their relative to the police, especially as it may all end in their mother or father being sent to prison. But it's your body and you shouldn't have to put up with a sexual relationship if you don't want to. If you can't cope with the problem, try to find someone sympathetic to talk it over with, perhaps your doctor, teacher or an older friend. It probably isn't a good idea to tell your other parent because they're likely to be very upset, angry, hurt, and unable to cope with the situation. If you have no one to confide in there are organisations which will be able to help you such as The Albany Trust or The National Council for Civil Liberties. A girl can also go to a women's centre for support.

If your doctor or social worker discovers you have had an incestuous relationship, she or he may want to tell the police, but not always. They will probably want to take steps to make sure that it doesn't happen again. This could mean that you'll be put into the care of the local authority.

Paedophilia (pronounced Pee-do-fillia)

Paedophiles are women and men — and in our society they're mostly men — who feel sexually attracted to young children. They get their sexual pleasure from looking at pictures of young children, or from touching a child's sex organs, and they often like a child to touch theirs. A paedophile may want to have sexual intercourse or buggery. It is a crime for an adult to have any form of sexual contact with a child, and paedophiles are usually sent to prison for many years.

Just as there are adult heterosexuals, homosexuals and bisexuals who harm each other and like to take advantage over another person, there are paedophiles who harm young children or who are indifferent to how they're affecting them — which is why we're all brought up never to accept lifts or presents from strangers.

It's obviously very difficult to know about the possible mental damage that is done to a child when an adult has sex with them or approaches them sexually. Though there are young children who seem to enjoy a sexual relationship with an adult, very many become frightened and confused by it and end up feeling guilty and scared about sex, perhaps for the rest of their lives. Everyone should have the right to say no or yes to a sexual relationship, and it's never going to be easy for a young child to say no to someone who is so much older and seems so much wiser and more powerful.

If an adult forces you to do something sexual that you don't want, you can report them to the police, although you may well find this very difficult if the adult is a family friend or a teacher. If you're worried or upset about a sexual experience you've had, either recently or when you were much younger, you'll find it helpful if you can talk about it with someone who is sympathetic and unshockable — an understanding friend, a school counsellor or a sex therapist in a clinic (see page 115).

Pornography & censorship

Pornography is erotic material — books, pictures, films — that makes people feel sexually aroused. 'Soft-core' porn usually means pictures of naked women and men (usually women) very much like the sort of photos you can see every day in the *Sun* and *Daily Mirror* newspapers. 'Girlie' magazines such as *Playboy* and *Penthouse* go a little further in what they describe and show, but they're usually thought to come into the soft-core category. 'Hard-core' porn goes much further and has detailed pictures and descriptions of every sexual activity you can think of, leaving nothing to the imagination.

The law tends to turn a blind eye to soft-core but it does try to ban hard-core pornography from being sent through the post, from being brought into the country and from being sold in shops. Other laws makes it a risky business to show pornographic films or 'blue movies' in public cinemas or private clubs.

Pornography and censorship are very controversial issues. There are those who would like to see all porn banned because so much of it does tend to emphasize the crude physical aspects of sexual relationships. Those who argue against censorship believe that the banning of porn can do more harm than the porn itself — that censorship laws make many people feel that it's wrong and depraved to feel sexually aroused, and that sexual satisfaction has therefore to be got 'under cover'.

In fact there's no reliable evidence which proves that looking at and enjoying porn results in sex crimes or crimes of violence. Indeed, there are doctors and sex therapists who give erotic material to patients with sex problems to help them learn how to get sexually aroused.

One of the main problems about porn is that most of it is produced for men by men who just want to make large profits. Because of the kind of society we live in, this means that much of it makes the women look like dumb performing animals or concentrates on pictures which relate sex with violence – which obviously many people find disgusting. A lot of porn confirms the widespread belief that it is enjoyable to treat women as nothing more than sex objects.

Another problem is that it's very difficult, especially if we live in a city, to avoid looking at porn, even if we try. We should all have the right to decide how and when we want to look at erotic material or think about sex, but our daily popular papers, advertising hoardings and posters outside strip clubs, some pubs and cinemas give us very little choice.

Laws which attempt to ban totally all pornography have little effect other than to push up the price of erotic books and films and to make many people feel guilty about their desire to be sexually aroused. Making porn illegal certainly does nothing to change the nature of erotic material. A society in which women were treated more as equals and which was less disapproving of people wanting to be sexually excited would perhaps produce erotic material which didn't rely on material so degrading to women.

Prostitution (also called whoring)

The large majority of prostitutes are women who agree to have sex with a man for a sum of money. There are also a very small number of men prostitutes who have women clients, and there are gay and bisexual prostitutes. Few women who become prostitutes ever had much choice about their work – the majority needed money and had no other way of earning it. A few of them are exploited by men called 'ponces' who set them up in business, make it difficult for them to stop working, and who take most of their money off them.

In the UK, prostitution itself isn't exactly illegal, but there are so many offences that can be committed only by a prostitute or by those involved in the organisation of prostitution that it might as well be.

Paying for sex won't give either the client or the prostitute any idea of how good a loving, caring and mutually sharing sexual relationship can be. Prostitutes are generally made to feel like sex objects by their clients, (think of the way people use the word 'whore'), like criminals by the law and like outcasts by the rest of society. Clients are made to feel as if a natural need for sex is a crime.

In some countries prostitution has been made legal and there are state brothels (a brothel is any building in which prostitutes work). This means that sexually transmitted diseases can be kept in check more easily, that prostitutes can earn a living wage, and that they're not terrorised by their pimps. But although legalised prostitution might be a way of ending some of the more obvious ways in which prostitutes are exploited, it doesn't solve the basic problem – that any sexual relationship which involves the buying and selling of sex has to be an unequal relationship. In a system of nationalised prostitution the role of the pimp has simply been transferred from a private individual to the local council or government.

There are people, women and men, who for a variety of reasons either can't or don't want any emotional involvement in their sexual relationships. But nor do they necessarily want their sex lives to consist entirely of masturbation. Prostitution, whether it's legal or illegal, whether it's privately organised or state run, isn't any sort of solution to this problem. But at least if prostitutes don't have to work on the fringes of the criminal world, as they do in the UK, perhaps fewer prostitutes would be made to feel like criminals and fewer of their clients would be made to feel guilty about their need for sex.

Rape

When a man rapes a woman, it means he forces her to have sexual intercourse with him against her will. The law against rape is intended to protect women from being harmed, but the way in which it actually works makes many raped or sexually assaulted women feel as if they are the criminal. There is often a suspicion in the back of people's minds that it is impossible for a woman to be raped and so they must be co-operating in some way, that women enjoy being treated roughly, and that a woman might have asked for rape by her manner or the clothes she is wearing. It's part of the double standard we still live with – men can wear what they like, walk where they like without fear of being raped, while women can be accused of 'asking' for rape by looking good or walking alone at night. One of the things many girls feel deprived of is travelling alone or going to places alone at night because in the back of their mind is a fear of rape or assault. This is a much more common fear than people think. Part of the problem is that there are a lot of ways in which sex is connected with violence in our society, in films, books, newspapers etc, which allows some people to assume that women want violence in sex. This is an awful assumption.

Rape is a horrible crime and no woman ever wants to be raped. Anyone who has been raped or has read in any detail what rape is like would realise this immediately. First of all, it's very frightening to have a man, usually stronger than yourself, forcing you to have sex by threatening perhaps to kill or disfigure you if you refuse. And you can't just cross your legs and tell your rapist to go away. Also, rape often involves being peed on, spat on, or hit, as well as being sexually assaulted. And quite apart from these other things it doesn't take much imagination to realise how awful it is simply to be forced to have intercourse without at all wanting to.

The law on rape is complicated. It has to be proved that the woman did not agree to have sexual intercourse. The man can try to prove that he didn't realise that she didn't want sex. It doesn't matter whether or not he ejaculated, but it does have to be proved that his penis penetrated her vagina. The woman can also use as evidence that he deliberately gave her drinks or drugs to make her incapable of resisting. The law assumes that a boy under fourteen is incapable of intercourse (although this is of course not true) but he can be prosecuted for attempted rape or sexual assault. According to the law a man 'cannot' rape his wife.

The maximum penalty for rape is life imprisonment and for attempted rape it's seven years. In practice, sentences are much lower and around the two year mark.

If you are being raped – some guidelines

Try to stay as calm as you can. Remember what the man looks like. (He may or may not be someone you know). If you think you might be badly hurt, don't struggle. Say, if you can, that you don't want sexual intercourse (or words like that). The main points are to get hurt as little as possible and to make it clear that you don't want sex.

Do you report the rape?

In principle it's a good idea to report the rape to the police. This might discourage some rapists who get away with it and do it again. But you have to be brave to report it. Very often, the ordeal that you go through once you have reported it is so unpleasant that it's understandable why many women prefer to keep quiet about it. In court, the man's lawyer may try to make out a case that the woman is immoral or promiscuous, that she led him on, that because she didn't struggle she's lying about being raped – and many other nasty accusations. You can be asked many searching questions about your previous sex life and if you're over 18 you may find the popular press will splash your personal misery all over the front pages in order to sell more copies of their papers.

If you decide to report it to the police:

– tell the police as soon as possible; delay may go against your case.
– if you can, tell someone what has happened – you may need a witness to your distress.
– don't wash, tidy yourself up or change your clothing; you may destroy valuable evidence. Don't have a bath because if there is any semen this will be used in evidence.
– don't take any alcohol or drugs.
– contact a friend, your parents or if you live in London, the Rape Crisis Centre (address and number, page 120) so that someone can go with you and give you moral support during the police and medical procedures.
– take a change of clothing with you, the police may keep some of your original clothing for tests and evidence.

- be prepared for a medical examination. You can ask for your own doctor or a woman doctor to be present.
- you can ask for your name to be withheld.

Whether or not you report to the police:

- talk to someone about what happened – you need a friend at this time.
- see a doctor to check for pregnancy, possible injuries and for sexually transmitted diseases.

In London there is the Rape Crisis Centre with a crisis phone line open twenty-four hours (01-360 6145). This centre gives all the help any raped or sexually assaulted women could need. It's free and totally confidential. They'll send a counsellor along with you to the police station if you want. If you need a friendly sympathetic solicitor they'll help you find one.

Transexuality

A transexual is someone who identifies with the opposite sex and who changes their sex. This identification usually takes place at a very young age. It's not illegal to be a transexual but, before the change is made many are treated as transvestites and find themselves in trouble with the law (see below).

To change sex totally, hormone treatment and several major operations are needed. A woman will need her internal reproductive organs (womb, Fallopian tubes and ovaries) removed to stop her periods, her breasts removed and the equivalent of a penis grafted on. A man will need to be given breasts and to have his penis and balls removed and replaced by something like a vagina. It will not be possible for either of you to have babies. Several discussion sessions with an experienced therapist will be needed.

By law, no doctor can give any of this treatment until you're 18. It can be done free on the NHS – although this is rare. You own doctor may or may not be very sympathetic. The Albany Trust (address, page 118) will give you all the help and assistance you need and put you in touch with your nearest transexual hospital unit.

Transvestism

People who like to wear the clothes of the opposite sex (called wearing drag) are transvestites. Some dress up like this in order to get sexually aroused, many do it simply in order to feel more 'themselves' and less tense. The law usually ignores women transvestites and male entertainers who perform drag acts, but men who like to wear women's clothes and make-up can find themselves in trouble with the law for 'insulting behaviour' or 'causing a breach of the peace', which carry punishments of up to 6 months.

110

If you are a transvestite, don't risk dressing up in public places unless it's somewhere that other transvestites go. You can get reported to the police for going into the 'wrong' toilet.

If you're worried about being a transvestite, or think you might be and want to talk to someone, contact the Albany Trust (page 118) or visit a sex therapist at a clinic (see page 115).

Voyeurism

Voyeur is the French word for someone who looks. In a sexual sense it means someone who gets sexually aroused by looking at people undressing or having sex. The law usually concerns itself with male voyeurs – but women get turned on this way too. Voyeurs often satisfy their sexual urges by peeping through key holes, looking through windows or by hanging around public toilets and changing rooms in shops and swimming pools. Voyeurs can be charged with 'insulting behaviour' or 'causing a breach of the peace', which carry punishments of up to 6 months.

It can be frightening to be watched especially if there's someone crawling outside your window or up a tree outside your bedroom; and it's never pleasant to be treated as a sex object. If you don't like it, apart from trying to make sure that you can't be seen in the future, you can also report the incident to the police. If you're worried about being a voyeur, you can talk to a sex therapist at a clinic (see page 115).

Dealing with the law

If you do get into trouble with the police, the following rules will help you:

— you should be told of the reason for your arrest – if you're not, ask so that you can be absolutely clear in your own mind what you're supposed to have done.

— at the police station you have the right to telephone a friend, lawyer or organisation. Ask if you can use the phone – you should be allowed to make one call although sometimes permission is not granted.

— you don't have to answer any questions apart from giving your name and address. Obviously police don't take too kindly to anyone who is very unhelpful but *remember*: most people are convicted because of what they have said at the police station. NEVER say that you're guilty. DON'T discuss the matter with which you've been charged unless a solicitor of your choice is present.

— you are allowed to ask for, and should be given, paper and pencil so that you can make notes about the way in which you were arrested. This may help you when you do meet a solicitor and are in court.

— all police officers must identify themselves before searching you in the street. They can search you only if they believe that you have committed a serious crime or are in possession of drugs or firearms. Girls can only be

searched by female police officers.
* you can't be forced to go to or remain in a police station unless you've been arrested. There's no such thing as arrest for questioning.
* if you are arrested, ask for bail. This means you can live at home while you're waiting for your trial. It should be granted unless the offence is very serious.

What to do in court

You are allowed to defend yourself in court without a solicitor – although you're more likely to be convicted if you do. The best plan is to get a lawyer to defend you. The law is complicated and can be very expensive. There is a scheme for free or cheap legal aid. How much it'll cost you depends on how much money you earn.

Where to get legal advice

Solicitors

Can advise you and help on a wide range of legal problems. They don't all work under the legal aid scheme. To find one that will, ask at the Citizen's Advice Bureau for one in your area, or ask an official at your local Magistrates' or County Court.

Law Society Legal Aid Area Office

Look up in telephone directory for your nearest office. You can find out from these offices how to go about getting legal aid.

Neighbourhood Law Centres

Many towns now have these centres which give free legal advice and assistance. If they can't solve your particular problem they'll tell you where you can go. Look up in phone directory or ask Citizen's Advice Bureau.

National Council for One Parent Families

Helps single mothers and fathers with their legal problems. (address, page 118).

The National Council for Civil Liberties

This is very helpful if you have a specific problem concerning your rights. They have part-time officers to help gays and women. (address, page 118).

Campaign for Homosexual Equality (CHE)

Gives legal help to gays, bisexuals, transexuals and transvestites (address, page 119).

Release

Helps young people on a wide range of legal problems – especially drug problems. (address, page 114).

USEFUL ADDRESSES

The following organisations, addresses and telephone numbers were all checked at the time this book went to the printers, but it is possible that some of the information will be out of date by the time you read it. If you have any difficulty in getting hold of any of these organisations, either contact a similar sounding organisations or ask at your local Citizen's Advice Bureau.

General Help and Advice

British Association for Counselling
26 Bedford Square, London WC1
01-636 4066
Will provide an up-to-date list of local counselling and advisory centres that can give you expert advice and help on problems concerning sex, drugs, accommodation and other mattters. Send 90p (this includes postage) to above address.

Citizen's Advice Bureau (CAB)
In most towns and cities. Look up address and number in phone book. Gives free and confidential advice on a wide range of subjects including legal aid, welfare benefits, how to fill in forms and where you can find other organisations which can help. You can phone or go to any CAB — not just your local one.

Contact
13 West Moreland Street, Dublin 2. Dublin 784188
Offers a free and confidential counselling service to young people on a wide range of subjects including accommodation, sex, drugs, home life etc.

Equal Opportunities Commission (EOC)
Quay Street, Manchester 3.
061-833 9244
Gives free advice, information and leaflets on all aspects of sexual equality.

Legal Action Group
28a Highgate Road, London NW5. Can give you the address of your nearest Neighbourhood Law Centre and the name and address of a sympathetic solicitor in your area.

National Council for Civil Liberties
186 Kings Cross Road, London WC1. 01-278 4575
A campaigning organisation to safeguard our rights and freedoms. Will give free and confidential information and advice on matters concerning legal aid, drugs, sex, homosexuality, women's rights, how to deal with the police etc. sae for booklist.

Newtownabbey Youth Counselling Service
Mossgrove Primary School, Swanston Estate, Glengormly, Newtownabbey, Co Antrim. Glengormley 40971
An experimental counselling service for young people aged 14-21. Mainly

a phone-in operation. Contact through school secretary between 9am–5pm and 7pm–9pm Monday and Wednesday. Deals with all personal problems whatever your race or religion. Will put you in contact with other organisations which help.

Release
1 Elgin Avenue, London W9 (office hours: 01-289 1123; emergency 24 hour phone service: 01-603 8654) Provides free advice and information on legal matters, drugs, housing, birth control, abortion, family, single parents, marriage, personality and personal problems etc. Campaigns for cannabis law reform. Can put you in touch with organisations that can help you in your area. sae for booklist.

Samaritans
Branches all over UK. Look up in phone book. Helps the lonely, suicidal or despairing. Phone in if you want to talk about any problems. You don't have to give your name or address.

Education

Advisory Centre for Education (ACE)
18 Victoria Park Square, Bethnal Green, London E9. 01-980 4596 Will give you a rundown on your rights on all aspects of education, ie. if you are pregnant and under school-leaving age, if you're expelled etc. Write or phone for free advice. Information sheets available at varying prices.

Children's Rights Workshop
73 Balfour Street, London SE17. 01-01-703 7217 Will give advice and information on non-sexist and non-biased children's books.

Department of Education and Science
Elizabeth House, 39 York Road, London SE1. Ask for information department. Can tell you what your rights in education are under the various Education Acts. Various free leaflets.

Health

U & I Club
22 Garrard Road, Islington, London N1. Advises on all aspects of urinary infections. Leaflets on cystitis and yeast infection (thrush). sae for booklist.

Community Health Councils (CHC)
Look up your local CHC in the phone book, under Community Health Councils. They can advise you on your medical rights, help you make a complaint and tell you where to go for advice on abortion, contraception, sexually transmitted diseases and drug problems.

Health Education Council
78 New Oxford Street, London WC1. 01-637 1881 For information on all aspects of health education. Issues free leaflets on sexually transmitted diseases, hygiene, sexual development, contraception, drugs etc. sae to above address or look up in phone book for local branch.

National Patients Association
11 Dartmouth Street, London SW1
01-222 4992
A voluntary pressure group which
handles cases of patients who want
to make a complaint about some
aspect of medical treatment or who
don't know where or how to get
medical treatment for some specific
illness. Very helpful to young people.
Free and confidential. sae for
booklist.

Sexually Transmitted Diseases
Special Clinics

Treatment centres for STDs usually
listed in phone book under Venereal
Disease or VD or under names
mentioned on page 89. Easiest way
to find your local clinic is to phone
your local hospital or doctor and
ask for address and phone number.

Women's National Cancer Control
Campaign (WNCCC)
9 Lang Street, London WC2.
01-836 9901
Provides information on cancer and
how to get treatment. Has free
leaflets including some on how to
check for breast cancer. Film 'Your
life in your hand' is available for
schools and interested groups.

Pregnancy

(Birth control, pregnancy testing,
abortion etc.)

Family Planning Association (FPA)
Head Office: 27-35 Mortimer Street,
London W1. 01-636 7866
For your nearest FPA clinic look up
in phone book or contact above
address. Provides free and
confidential advice and information

for girls and boys on birth control,
abortion, sexual problems, and a
service of regular medical supervision, cervical smear testing and
pregnancy testing. Issues a wide
range of free leaflets and posters on
birth, birth control, sexually transmitted diseases, and all aspects of
sexual relationships, sae for
booklist.

Family Planning Association of
Northern Ireland
47 Botanic Avenue, Belfast B7.
Belfast 25488
You can go to any of the 22 clinics
in Northern Ireland regardless of
where you live. Provides same service
as FPA above.

Irish Family Planning Association
15 Mountjoy Square, Dublin 1.
Dublin 744133 or 688697
59 Synge Street, Dublin 8.
Dublin 682420
Both clinics provide information and
advice on birth control, sexual
problems, pregnancy testing and they
offer a pregnancy counselling service.
Very helpful and sympathetic to
women and girls with unwanted
pregnancies. Fees according to how
much you earn. Phone one of the
above numbers to see if there is a
branch in your area. Phone first for
an appointment.

Family Planning Centre
10 Merion Square, Dublin.
Dublin 767852
Open Monday – Friday, 12 pm –
6pm. Phone for an appointment. A
private clinic charging a fee, so check
prices. Provides full advice service
about birth control and supplies,
pregnancy testing, sexual problems
etc. Contraceptives available by
post. Refers girls wanting

pregnancy terminations to good clinics in England.

British Pregnancy Advisory Service
Aust Manor, Wooton Wawen, Solihull, West Midlands, B95 6DA
Henley-in-Arden 3225
A non-profit making charitable organisation. Clinics in many towns and cities, offering pregnancy tests, counselling, birth control, pregnancy and abortion advice. Completely sympathetic to young people and their problems. Look up in phone book or contact above address for your nearest branch.
Current charges: abortion – £66; birth control – free or £3 per year (plus cost of supplies) depending on where you live; pregnancy testing – £2. Can arrange a generous loan and grant system for those unable to afford the abortion fee. Provide overnight and outpatient abortion facilities at their own excellent nursing homes. Write to above address for literature (free) and films on birth control and abortion.

Brook Advisory Centre
Head office: 233 Tottenham Court Road, London W1. 01-580 2991/323 1522
Centres also in Birmingham, Cambridge, Coventry, Edinburgh, London and Liverpool.
Gives birth control advice and counselling to young people with sexual problems. Completely confidential. Consultation and birth control supplies free at most centres. Fee charged for pregnancy testing and infection testing at some of the centres. (But no one is refused just because they have no money). Ring, write or call in.

Grapevine
296 Holloway Road, London N7.
(office hours: 01-607 0949; information and advice answer phone: 01-607 0935)
A free sex education advice and information service for young people. Provides support and counselling for anyone with sex and personal problems. Sends trained workers into schools, youth clubs and community groups. Will put you in touch with other useful organisations.

Marie Stopes Memorial Clinic
108 Whitfield Street, London W1.
01-388 0662
Named after one of the original campaigners for birth control. Privately run clinic for women and men of all ages. Gives expert and sympathetic advice on birth control, pregnancy testing, abortion and any sexual problems. Not free – but inexpesnive. sae for list of charges.

National Marriage Guidance Council
Herbert Gray College, Little Church Street, Rugby, Warwickshire.
0788 72341
Runs clinics for couples over 16 (married or not) with sexual, marriage or relationship problems. Contact above address or look up in phone book for your nearest branch.

Pregnancy Advisory Service
40 Margaret Street, London W1.
01-409 0281
London-based registered charity providing much the same service as British Pregnancy Advisory Service (see above).

Westminster Youth Advisory Service
21 Portnall Road, London W9.
01-969 3825
Offers young people practical help,
information and advice on problems
concerning sex, pregnancy, abortion
or any personal problem. Free,
private and confidential.

**Ulster Pregnancy Advisory
Association Ltd.**
338a Lisburn Road, Belfast 9.
0232-667345
Has a free answering service. Provides
testing and counselling service for
pregnant girls. Arranges low-cost
abortions in England through the
British Pregnancy Advisory Service
(see page   ).

Adoption, Fostering, Single Parents

Adoption Resource Exchange (ARE)
40 Brunswick Square, London WC1.
01-837 0496
Contact ARE to find adoption
agencies who work together to find
homes for children with special
needs.

Ally
Dominican Priory, Upper Dorset
Street, Dublin 1. Dublin 740300
Offers a sympathetic service for
single pregnant girls. Runs a family
placement scheme for girls to live
with a friendly family while they're
pregnant. Free after-care and advice.

**Association of British Adoption and
Fostering Agencies**
4 Southampton Row, London WC1
01-242 8951
Source of information and advice
during pregnancy on the choice to be
made between adoption and

fostering. Free leaflet: *Single and
Pregnant*. (includes a list of adoption
agencies throughout UK). Send sae.

**Catholic Protection and Rescue
Society**
30 South Anne Street, Dublin 2.
Dublin 779664
Geared to helping single pregnant
girls. Can provide care for dependent
babies in the form of temporary
residential and nursery care. Can
arrange adoptions. Free and
confidential.

Cherish
2 Lower Pembroke Street, Dublin 2.
Dublin 682744
10am–9pm Monday, 10am–5.30pm
Tuesday–Friday.
Mary Kerrigan, 111 Tradaree Court,
Shannon, Co Clare. Limerick 61989
–after 6pm
Mainly for girls wanting to keep their
babies, but also offers pregnancy
counselling service, advice and
accommodation during and after
pregnancy.

Claimants' Union
Groups of people receiving social
security or unemployment benefit.
They fight for claims at social
security offices, appeal tribunals
and in courts. Ask at CAB for your
local branch.

Gingerbread
34 Wellington Street, London WC2
38 Berkeley Square, Glasgow.
A self-help group for one parent
families with 300 branches
throughout the UK. sae for booklist.

International Adoption Society
160 Peckham Rye, London SE22
01-693 9611
Counselling service for single
pregnant girls. Will arrange adoption

and pays particular attention to your choice of family you'd like your child placed in.

National Childbirth Trust
9 Queensborough Terrace, London W2. 01-229 9319
Offers friendly advice to pregnant girls about childbirth, before and after the birth and about breast feeding. Aims to take all the fear out of childbirth. Encourages the fathers to take part. Issues leaflets and booklist on pregnancy, childbirth and breast feeding. sae for details of nearest class and charges.

National Council for One Parent Families
255 Kentish Town Road, London NW5. 01-267 1361
Sympathetic, helpful and expert advice on all matters concerning single mothers and fathers. Offers advice without strings or pressures. Acts as a link between those who need information or advice and self help organisations and groups, local social workers, and other people who have the responsibility of providing services for one parent families and single pregnant girls. Enquiries dealt with by letter, phone or interview (best to book an appointment) – all private and confidential. Will put you in touch with other useful organisations.

National Fostercare Association
5 Talacre Road, Kentish Town, London NW5. 01-485 8201
Provides help advice and information for girls who want their child fostered.

Parent to Parent Information Adoption Services
26 Belsize Grove, London NW3 01-722 9996

Write or phone for information about adoption agencies.

St. Anne's Adoption
Assumption Road, Cork. Cork 51407/52747
Catholic organisation set up to help unmarried mothers with information about adoption and fostering.

Scottish Council for Single Parents
44 Albany Street, Edinburgh EH1 031-556 3899
Friendly, sympathetic and helpful advice and information on all problems for lone parents and single pregnant girls. Free.

Single Handed Ltd.
68 Lewes Road, Haywards Heath, Sussex. 0444-54663
A privately run organisation helping single parents find accommodation by introducing them to other single parents who want to share, providing a link with other single parents and residential jobs.

Sexual Identity

Albany Trust
16-20 Strutton Ground, London SW1. 01-222 0701
Charitable organisation concerned with educational research and the psycho-sexual health of people whatever their age. Provides a counselling service for those with problems relating to homosexuality, bisexuality, transexuality, transvestism, paedophilia or any sexual identity problem. Normal office hours. Free. sae for booklist.

Beaumont Society
BM Box 3084, London WC1V 6XX
Charitable organisation providing free help and counselling service for transvestites.

Campaign for Homosexual Equality (CHE)
Po Box 427, 33 King Street, Manchester 6. 061-228 1985
CHE has over 120 local groups in England and Wales. Provides social activities and, for those who want it, a chance to join their campaigning work to achieve full legal and social equality for gay women and men of all ages. Membership open to all who support their aims. Contact above address for information about your local gay, transvestite, transexual groups. Very helpful and friendly. Provides a legal advice service. Free.

Friend
c/o CHE (see above)
National telephone befriending service is available on 01-359 7371/2 from 7.30pm – 10pm each night. Exists to help gay and bisexual women and men and all those with problems of sexual identity of all ages who feel they have no one to turn to. Confidential and very understanding to young people. Free.

Gay Christian Movement
c/o 15 Bermuda Road, Cambridge
Has several groups in England for gays of all ages and of any Christian denomination.

Gay News
1a Normand Gardens, Greyhound Road, London W14. 01-381 2161
Excellent fortnightly newspaper for gays and all those interested. Regularly provides up to date gay guide to clubs, pubs, switchboards etc in UK.

Gay Switchboard
5 Caledonian Road, London N1. 01-01-837 7324
Twenty-four-hour-a-day phone and help service for gays. A kind of gay 'citizens advice bureau', they provide information on all aspects of the gay world as well as running a free flat-sharing service, dealing with emotional problems, legal emergencies, and chatting to the lonely. Warning: There has been another switchboard operated by an organization which disapproves. Check out each switchboard at above address or contact CHE or Gay News.

Icebreakers
BM/Gay Lib, London WC1. 01-270 9590
Phone advice service and youth therapy group in London and some other towns for all those with sexual identity problems. Phone any evening between 7.30pm – 10.30pm. Women answer on Wednesdays.

Irish Gay Rights Movement.
Administration Office, Parnell Square, West Dublin. Dublin 764240
Phone Thursdays between 7.30pm – 8.30pm and Saturdays 3pm – 6pm. Advice and help for gays in Eire.

Northern Ireland Gay Rights Association
4 University Street, Belfast 7
Free help, advice and information for gays of all ages.

Sappho
The Basement, 20 Dorset Square, London NW1 01-742 3636
Sappho is a lesbian/feminist magazine published every month by gay women for all women. Contact Sappho for subscription and information about their groups and other lesbian groups in your area.

Scottish Minorities Group

60 Broughton Street, Edinburgh EH1
031-556 4049
A membership organisation
campaigning for a better deal for
Scottish homosexuals. Has several
branches in Scotland that provide up-
to-date information about social
events of interest to sexual minorities
and a free legal advice service.

Parents Enquiry

Rose Robertson, 16 Horley Road,
Catford, Lonodn SE6
Parents of gay children can get
extremely good and helpful advice
and information on what it means to
be gay.

Quest

c/o The Secretary, 8d South Park
Road, Raynes Park, London SW19
Roman Catholic group for gays of
all ages.

Women's Movement

There are women's centres in many
towns throughout the UK which
provide a way for groups and
individual women to get together.
Some offer services such as
pregnancy testing, advice on
abortion, pregnancy, motherhood,
lesbianism etc. They welcome all
women of any age and not just those
who count themselves as being in the
women's movement. To find your
nearest group contact any of the
following:

A Woman's Place

42 Earlham Street, London WC2
01-836 6081
For information about groups in
London.

Scottish Women's Liberation Workshop

4 Fleming Place, St Andrews, Fife,
Scotland.
Information centre for the women's
movement in Scotland.

Spare Rib

27 Clerkenwell Close, London EC1
01-253 9792
Monthly magazine on women's
issues. Available on most bookstalls
or contact above address to find out
about subscription rates. Publishes
each month, details about women's
campaigns, meetings and social
events. Write to *Spare Rib* asking for
contacts in your area.

Wires

c/o 36 Blenheim Terrace, Leeds 2.
Produces a fortnightly newsletter
packed with information on women's
issues and details about local groups.

Women in Rural Wales

Geulan Felen, Pentre Cwrt,
Llandyssul, Dyfed.
A contact centre for women living in
rural Wales interested in the women's
movement who want to make
contact with other women living near
them.

Rape Crisis Centre

PO Box 42, London N6 5BU (Office
hours: 01-340 6913; 24-hour
emergency service: 01-340 6145.
Provides moral support, legal and
medical advice and counselling for
raped or sexually assaulted women of
any age. Wherever you live, phone
the emergency service number at any
time, day or night, to talk with
someone who will be helpful,
friendly and sympathetic. The Centre

can arrange tests for pregnancy and sexually transmitted diseases and will go with you (if you live in London) to the clinic, doctor, police station and court. Will not put any pressure on you to report to the police. Write to above address for more information on rape.

BOOKLIST

Many of the organisations mentioned in the previous section will send you free or low-priced leaflets on the subjects they deal with..It's best to send a stamped addressed envelope to them to get either their leaflets or their list of publications. The following books and publications will give you further information and many of them have good lists of other books you can read.

Abortion Law Reform Society, *A Woman's Right to Choose*, ALRA 1975.
A campaigning leaflet on abortion.

Carol Adams and Rae Laurikietis, *The Gender Trap*. Book 1: *Education and Work;* Book 2: *Sex and Marriage*; Book 3: *Messages and Images*. Quartet 1976
Good and enjoyable books about the sex roles imposed on girls and boys in our society. Written for young people in schools, colleges and at work and for their teachers and parents. Each book has cartoons, poems, stories, extracts, interviews, questions and ideas for projects, discussion and debate.

Patricia Ashdown-Sharp, *The Single Woman's Guide to Pregnancy and Parenthood*, Penguin 1975
A comprehensive guide to pregnancy, sex, marriage, living together, abortion, adoption, fostering, bringing up a child on your own, contraception and lots more. Some of the information is now out of date but it is still a very useful book for both girls and boys.

Nan Berger, *Rights: A Handbook for People Under Age*, Penguin Education 1974
Clear, easy to read book with lovely illustrations on rights for young people at home, school, work, on the street and what to do if you get into trouble with the police etc.

David Blamine, *Homosexuality from the Inside*, Quaker Friendly Society
Easy-to-read booklet about what it's like to be gay.

Anna Coote & Tess Gill, *Women's Rights: A Practical Guide*, Penguin 1977
Everything you could want to know about women's rights in the fields of work, money, sex, marriage, divorce, separation, children, housing, consumerism, immigration, prison and the law etc. Good book list and list of addresses of useful organisations

Anna Coote & Tess Gill, *The Rape Controversy*, National Council for Civil Liberties 1976
50p leaflet on the law, the myths, the facts: changes that are needed and what to do if you are raped.

Anna Coote & Larry Grant, *Civil Liberty, the NCCL Guide*, National Council for Civil Liberties 1972
Everything you need to know about your rights and how to protect them.

Alex Comfort (ed) *The Joy of Sex*, Quartet Books 1974
Subtitle, 'A Gourmet Guide to Lovemaking'. Written for adults but is a good, easy-to-read and well illustrated account of how to enjoy sex.

Consumer's Association, *Pregnancy Month by Month* (1974), *New Born Baby* (1974) and *Sex with Health* (1972)
Clearly written to take all the worrying out of pregnancy, childbirth and birth control.

K. Dalton, *The Menstrual Cycle*, Penguin 1969
Detailed information on everything you could possibly want to know about periods.

Dr David Delvin, *Carefree Love, The Home Doctor's Guide to Safe Sex and the Pill*, New English Library 1976
Illustrated and comprehensive guide to birth control. Explains what to do if you don't have a contraceptive. Easy to read and often very funny. He supports the view, 'Don't trust to luck when you have a fuck!'

Diagram Group, *Woman's Body: An Owner's Manual* and *Man's Body: An Owner's Manual*, Paddington Press Ltd 1976/7
Beautifully clear and well illustrated books on how our bodies work in sickness and health.

Family Planning Association, *Learning to Live with Sex*, FPA Publications

Constantly being updated. Still refers to doctors as if they're all men, but one of the best short pamphlets on sex education from acne to wet dreams. For teenagers.

Carolyn Faulder, Christine Jackson, and Mary Lewis, *The Women's Directory*, Quartet 1976
A self-help guide to what women are doing and thinking in Britain today: including health, sexuality, marriage, children, rape, fostering, adoption, the women's movement, and lots more. Good contacts list of helpful organisations, and reading list.

Gingerbread, *One Parent Families – A Finer Future*, Gingerbread 1973
(The Finer Report was produced by a Royal Commission, on one-parent families and made many good recommendations, few of which have become law). All about your rights as a single parent.

Germaine Greer, *The Female Eunuch*, Paladin 1971
Probably for the slightly older teenager, but quite easy to read. Funny/serious and campaigning book. A good introduction to the ideas behind the women's movement.

Soren & Jasper Jensen, *The Little Red Schoolbook*, Stage 1 1971
Easy-to-read, clear information at basic level about rights, education, sex and drugs for young people. There was an attempt to ban this book – it criticises adult behaviour and the attempts by adults to control young people – it wasn't banned, although parts had to be cut.

Angela Kilmartin, *Understanding Cystitis*, Pan 1975
Everything you could want to know

about cystitis (see page 96) and related illnesses. Written by the founder of the U & I Club (see page 114).

ed. Angela Phillips & Jill Rakusen, *Our Bodies, Ourselves*, Penguin 1978
A lot of valuable information on all aspects of women's health and sexuality: anatomy, sexuality, relationships, nutrition, exercise, health, venereal disease, contraception, parenthood, childbirth, menopause, self defence, rape and many other topics. Personal accounts included.

Theodor Rosebury, *Microbes and Morals: A Study of VD*, Paladin 1975
Probably for the slightly older teenager, but a very non-technical book by a doctor with a good sense of humour who believes that sex is natural and good but disease is unnatural and bad.

Michael Schofield, *The Sexual Behaviour of Young People* and *The Sexual Bahaviour of Young Adults*, Penguin 1973
Written for adults but packed with very readable information about what young people think about sex.

Dr Basil Stoll, *But Why Cancer, Sally*, Heinemann 1974
Easy to read book for girls and boys on all aspects of cancer. Very reassuring. Some of the proceeds to to the Women's National Cancer Control Campaign (see page 115).

INDEX

abortion, 70, 71; 72, 75-80, 105; addresses of helpful organisations, 115-7
acne, *see* spots
adolescence, 3
adoption, 71, 84; addresses of helpful organisations, 117-8
Adoption Resource Exchange, 117
Advisory Centre for Education, 85, 114
Age of Consent, 41, 72, 102-3; *see also* under sixteen
A.I.D., *see* Artificial Insemination
Albany Trust, 105, 110, 111, 118
alcohol, 50
Ally, 117
american tips, contraceptive, 62
anal intercourse, 25, 40, 89, 103
anus, 34, 36, 40, 89
aphrodisiacs, 49
artificial insemination, 21, 25
asexuality, 23
Association of British Adoption and Fostering Agencies, 84, 117
aunty, *see* period
aureola, 8

baby, 13, 14, 20; having a baby, 81-86; addresses of helpful organisations, 117-118; *see also* fertilisation and conception
bad blood, *see* syphilis
balls, *see* testicles
bearded clam, *see* vagina
Beaumont Society, 118
beaver, *see* mons pubis
bestiality, 103
birth control, 35, 38, 41, 51-68; addresses of helpful organisations, 115-7
birth passage, *see* vagina
bisexuality, 23, 26
bladder, 10, 11, 18, 19; diseases connected with, 96, 97
blow job, *see* oral sex
bollocks, *see* testicles
bonk, being on the, *see* erection
boobs, *see* breasts

buds, *see* breasts
buggery, *see* anal intercourse
bra, 8
breasts, 5, 8, 34, 36, 38, 39; cancer and self examination, 99-100
breast feeding, 8
bringing yourself off, *see* masturbation
British Association for Counselling, 113
British Pregnancy Advisory Service, 78, 116
Brook Advisory Centre, 116
B.U.P.A., 77
bush, *see* mons pubis

C-film, contraceptive, 65
Campaign for Homosexual Equality, 112, 119
Cancer, 98-101; breast, 99-100; cervical, 61, 64, 100; penis and testicles, 101
Candidosis, *see* Thrush
cap, contraceptive, 54, 55, 62-64
Care Order, 82
Catholic Protection and Rescue, 117
censorship, 106-7
cervix, 14, 20, 47, 89; and cancer, 100
chancre, *see* soft sore
Cherish, 117
cherry, *see* hymen and virginity
Child Benefit Allowance, 85
Children's Rights Workshop, 114
circumcision, 11, 30, 97
Citizen's Advice Bureau (CAB), 82, 84, 85, 86, 89, 112, 133
Claimant's Union, 86, 117
clap, *see* gonorrhoea
climax, *see* orgasm
clitoris, 9, 10, 11, 27, 29, 33, 34, 39
cobblers, *see* testicles
cock, *see* penis
cock-cheese, *see* smegma
coil, contraceptive, 54, 59-60
coitus, *see* intercourse
coitus interruptus, *see* withdrawal
coitus reservatus, *see* holding back
come, coming, *see* ejaculation and . orgasm
Community Health Council, 114
conception, 21, 51; *see also* fertilisation
condom, contraceptive, *see* sheath

Contact (Dublin), 113
contact tracing, 90
contraception, *see* birth control
contraceptive, *see* birth control
crabs, *see* pubic lice
crack, *see* vagina
crush, 3
cunnilingus, 40
cunt, as a swear word, 9; *see also* vulva and vagina
curse, *see* period
cystitis, 96-7; addresses of helpful organisations, 114

D and C, Dilation and Curettage, 79; *see also* abortion
deodorants, 5, 40, 87; *see also* smell
Department of Education and Science, 114
Department of Health and Social Security, 85
dick, *see* penis
diaphragm, contraceptive, *see* cap, contraceptive
disease, for general information about disease, illness and infection *see* 87-101
dildoes, dildols, 29
dose, *see* syphilis
douche, 67
drag, *see* transvestism
drip, on, *see* period
drugs, 49; *see also* Release
durex, contraceptive, *see* sheath
Dutch cap, contraceptive, *see* diaphragm
dyke, *see* homosexuality and lesbianism

education, when pregnant, 84
egg cell, 13, 14, 15, 20
Eire; abortion in, 78; age of consent, 102; birth control in, 55; and marriage, 83; and homosexuality, 103
ejaculation, 13, 18, 19, 20, 27-31, 32, 36; premature, 48; *see also* orgasm
embryo, 10
epididymis, 18
Equal Opportunities Commission, 85, 113
erection, 10, 11, 12, 19, 20, 35, 36, 50
erogenous zones, 38
exhibitionism, 104

faggot, *see* homosexuality
fairy, *see* homosexuality
Fallopian Tubes, 13, 14, 20, 21, 51
Family Planning Association (London), 83, 100, 115
Family Planning Association of Northern Ireland, 115
Family Planning Centre (Dublin), 115
fanny, *see* vulva and vagina
fantasies, 20, 33
father of child, 86; reaction to pregnancy, 72; rights over child, 72, 84; maintenance payments, 86
fellatio, *see* oral sex
fertilisation, 13, 14, 20, 21, 51, 69; *see also* conception
fiddling, *see* masturbation
finger fucking, 39
foetus, 75
follicle, 13
foreplay, 42
foreskin, 11, 87; tight, 97; infections, 97; *see also* circumcision
fostering, 71, 84; addresses of helpful organisations, 117-18
french letter, contraceptive, *see* sheath
Friend, 119
frigidity, 47
fuck, *see* intercourse

gay, *see* homosexuality
Gay Christian Movement, 119
Gay Switchboard, 119
Gingerbread, 117
glans, clitoris, 10; penis, 11
gonorrhoea, 88, 90, 91-92, 94
Grapevine, 116
grecian tips, contraceptive, 62

hard on, *see* erection
hair, around breasts, 8; *see also* pubic hair
head, *see* oral sex
health, for general information on how to treat illness, disease and infection *see* 87-101; addresses of helpful organisations, 114-5
Health Education Council, 114
herpes, genital, 95
heterosexuality, 22-23, 37
holding back, 66-7
hole, *see* vagina

holy week, *see* period
homosexuality, 23, 24, 25, 89, 103
hormones, 3, 5, 13, 15, 18, 19, 56, 58
horny, *see* erection
hymen, 10, 11, 15, 16, 45, 46; *see also* virginity
hysterotomy, 79

Icebreakers, 119
infection, for general information about disease and infection *see* pages 87-101
International Adoption Society, 117
Intrauterine Device (IUD), *see* coil
intercourse, 10, 20, 34, 41-4, 51; under sixteen, 41; positions, 43-4; some problems, 45-50; *see also* age of consent
incest, 105
impotence, 48
Irish Family Planning Association (Dublin), 115
Irish Gay Rights Movement (Dublin), 119
itch, *see* scabies

jacking off, *see* masturbation
jam butties, *see* period
jerking off, *see* masturbation
jism, *see* semen
John Thomas, *see* penis
johnny, *see* sheath, contraceptive

kissing, 33, 38, 39, 40
knob, *see* penis
knockers, *see* breasts
KY Jelly, 16, 29, 47

labia, majora and minora, *see* vaginal lips
law and sex, 102-112; age of consent, 41, 102-3; anal intercourse, 40, 103; bestiality, 103; exhibitionism, 104; homosexuality, 25, 103, 104-5; incest, 105; paedophilia, 105-6; pornography and censorship, 106-7; prostitution, 107-8; rape, 108-110; transexuality, 110; transvestism, 110-111; voyeurism, 111; dealing with the law, 111-112; what to do in court, 112; where to get legal advice, 112; *see also* abortion, birth control, legal aid, living together, marriage under sixteen

lay, *see* intercourse
Legal Action Group, 113
legal aid, 84, 112
lesbianism, 21, 24, 25; *see also* homosexuality
lezz, *see* lesbianism
lice, *see* pubic lice
lips, inner and outer, *see* vaginal lips
living together, 83
love, 2, 3

maidenhead, *see* hymen and virginity
maintenance, 86
make love, *see* intercourse
man's best friend, *see* penis
marriage, 71, 83
Marie Stopes Memorial Clinic, 116
masturbation, 27-31, 32, 39
maternity benefit, 85
maturity, 3
menses, *see* period
menstrual period, *see* period
menstrual cycle, *see* period
menstrual extraction, 68
menstruation, *see* period
mini-pill, *see* pill
miscarriage, 70, 76
monilias yeast infection, *see* Thrush
mons pubis, 9, 10
mons veneris, *see* mons pubis
monthlies, time of the month, *see* period
morning sickness, 69
myths; birth control, 53, 54; circumcision, 11; female sexuality, 22, 28, 38, 47; femininity, 22; homosexuality, 23, 25; masculinity, 22; masturbation, 27-29, 30, 31; female orgasm; 33; periods, 17; ending unwanted pregnancy, 70; sexually transmitted diseases, 88; size of breasts, 8; size of penis, 11, 42; size of vagina, 42; sex aids, 48-50; venereal diseases, 90; virginity, 45, 46; male sexuality, 38, 48; intercourse, 41, 47; coming together, 43

National Childbirth Trust, 83, 118
National Council for Civil Liberties (NCCL), 82, 105, 112, 113
National Council for One Parent Families, 81, 82, 83, 84, 85, 86, 112, 118

National Fostercare Association, 118
National Marriage Guidance Council, 116
National Patients' Association, 115
neck of womb, *see* cervix
Newtownabbey Youth Counselling Service, 113
nipples, 8, 29, 33, 36, 38, 100
nits, *see* pubic lice
nocturnal emission, *see* wet dream
noddy, *see* sheath
Northern Ireland: abortion in, 78; age of consent in, 102; homosexuality in, 103; marriage in, 83
Northern Ireland Gay Rights Association, 119
nuts, *see* testicles
nymphomania, 47

One Parent Families, *see* National Association for One Parent Families
oral sex, 39-40, 89
orgasm, 27, 30, 31, 32-36, 39, 42-43, 44
os, 14, 20
ova, *see* egg cell
ovary, 3, 13
ovulation, 13
ovum, *see* egg cell

pansy, *see* homosexuality
paedophilia, 105-6
Parents' Enquiry, 120
Parent to Parent Information Adoption Service, 118
pee, 10, 18, 19
pee hole, *see* urethra
penis, 3, 9, 10, 11, 19, 27, 30, 32, 36, 39; diseases connected with, 86-93, 94, 95, 96, 97, 101
period, menstrual, 11, 13, 15, 17; missing, a symptom of pregnancy, 15, 69; pains and problems, 17, 18, 98
petting, 38-41
Pill, oral contraceptive, 54, 55, 56-8,; mini pill, 58, 60; before and after, 67; for men, 68
pills, pillocks, *see* testicles
pips, *see* breasts
playing with yourself, *see* masturbation
pornography and censorship, 106-7
pouf, *see* homosexuality

pox, *see* syphilis
pregnancy, 14, 15, 39, 69-74; sex without, 39; symptoms, 69; testing, 70-1; if unwanted, 71-4; medical care during, 82; education during, 73, 84; accommodation during, 81; under sixteen, 82; work during, 85; and money, 85-6; addresses of helpful organisations, 115-118
Pregnancy Advisory Service, 116
pre-menstrual tension, 98
prick, *see* penis
Private Patient's Plan, 77
prophylactic, *see* sheath
prostate gland, 18, 19
prostitution, 107-8
puberty, 3, 13, 18
pubes, *see* pubic hair
pubic hair, 5, 10, 13
pubic lice, 95
pubis, *see* mons pubis
pussy, *see* vulva and vagina

queen, *see* homosexuality
queer, *see* homosexuality
Quest, 120
quim, *see* vulva and vagina

rag, *see* period
rape, 108-110
Rape Crisis Centre, 109, 110, 120
Release, 82, 112, 114
reproductive organs: girls, 13; boys, 18, 19
rhythm method of birth control, 65-6

St. Anne's Adoption, 118
'Safe' method of birth control, *see* rhythm method
Samaritans, 114
sanitary towel, 15, 17
Sappho, 119
scabies, 95
Scotland, homosexuality illegal in, 103; marriage in, 83
Scottish Council for Single Parents, 118
Scottish Minorities Group, 119-120
Scottish Women's Liberation Workshop, 120
screw, *see* intercourse
scrotal sac, scrotum, 12
semen, 13, 18, 19, 20, 27, 32, 40
seminal ducts, 18, 19

seminal fluid, 18, 19
seminal vesicles, 18, 19
sex aids, 48-50
sex fluid, *see* semen
sex toys, 29-30, 40
sexual arousal (and excitement), 1, 10, 11, 18, 20, 27-31, 32-6, 38, 39
sexual intercourse, *see* intercourse
sexually transmitted diseases, 61, 88-94, 115
shag, *see* intercourse
sheath, contraceptive, 47, 54, 55, 60-2
shooting your load, *see* ejaculation
Single Handed Ltd., 118
sixty nine, *see* oral sex
slit, *see* vagina
smegma, 11, 87, 97
smells, 38, 39, 86; *see also* deodorants
sodomy, *see* anal intercourse
soft sore, 90
soixante neuf, *see* oral intercourse
solicitor, 112
Spare Rib, 120
Special Clinic, 88, 94, 95, 96, 115
sperm, 13, 18, 19, 20, 36, 51
spermicide, 54, 55, 61, 64-5
spots, 5
spunk, *see* semen
stereotyping, 22
sterilisation, 65
stones, *see* testicles
straight, *see* heterosexuality
supplementary benefit, 85
sweat, 5
syphilis, 88, 90, 92-3

Tampax, 17
tampon, 15, 16, 17, 46
testes, *see* testicles
testicles, 3, 10, 12, 18, 35, 36; diseases connected with, 97, 98, 101
Thrush, 88, 93
tits, titties, *see* breasts
tool, *see* penis
tossing off, *see* masturbation
transvestism, 110-111
transexuality, 110
Tribunal for Unfair Dismissal, 85
trichomoniasis (trich or TV), 88, 94
twat, *see* vagina
twins, 21

U & I Club, 97, 114
Ulster, *see* Northern Ireland
Ulster Pregnancy Advisory Association Ltd., 117
under sixteen; abortion, 73, 76, 82; birth control, 54, 55; education, 84; intercourse, 41, 102-3; leaving home, 82; medical treatment, 82; pregnancy, 71, 72, 82
unlawful sexual intercourse, *see* age of consent
urethra, girl, 9, 10; boy, 11, 18
urethritis, 94-5, 97
urine, *see* pee
uterus, *see* womb

vagina, 3, 9, 14, 20, 27, 29, 33, 34, 39, 47, 87; entrance to, 9, 10; and infections, 40, 47, 93-4
vaginal lips, 9, 10
vas deferens, 18
vasectomy, 65
venereal disease, 90-3; *see also* contact tracing, gonorrhoea, sexually transmitted diseases, special clinics, syphilis
vaginal fluid, 27, 34, 39, 47
vaginitis, non specific, 94
vibrators, 29
virginity, 45, 46
voice, breaking, 5
voyeurism, 111
vulva, 9, 10

wank, *see* masturbation
warts, genital, 88, 96
Westminster Youth Advisory Service, 117
wet dreams, 19, 20
willy, *see* penis
whoring, *see* prostitution

Wires, 120
withdrawal, method of birth control, 66
womb, 3, 10, 13, 20, 21, 47, 51
Women's National Cancer Control Campaign, 115
Women's centres, 71, 105; addresses of, 120-1
A Woman's Place, 120
Women in Rural Wales, 120

yeast infection, *see* Thrush
yellow body, 14